alone together

AN ANTHOLOGY

BIRMINGHAM CITY
University

Edited by
Vanessa Courtney, John Hunter,
Charlotte Newman and Shauntelle Trotter

Published by **Imprimata**
for and on behalf of The School of English, Birmingham City University.

First published 2015
Compilation © The School of English,
Birmingham City University 2015
Contributions © individual copyright holders

A CIP Catalogue record for this book is available
from the British library

ISBN 978-1-906192-88-4

Cover image, design and typesetting
by Mark Bracey @ Imprimata

Printed in Great Britain
InX-192884-15-01

Imprimata

An imprint of InXmedia Limited
Trident Court, 1 Oakcroft Road, Chessington, Surrey KT9 1BD, UK

Contents

Foreword

Though writers write alone, they're all in it together, and the paradox in the title of this anthology really isn't one, or not when it comes to the collective work of a creative writing group. When we think about it, which we do perhaps too much, a great deal of the writer's life seems paradoxical, not least because the most useful principles are the ones which aren't principles. 'There are three rules for writing a novel', Somerset Maugham is reputed to have told a writing class: 'Unfortunately, no one knows what they are'. We know what he means, though it may be a frustrating sort of truth to face.

It's true of pretty much every literary genre, and this anthology displays that: poems, dramas, film scripts, novels, stories, flash fiction and memoir. We write in the dark, but an anthology of our collective solitudes shows we are at least writing in a shared darkness. As someone who doesn't normally teach creative writing, working at Birmingham City University as a visiting Fellow of the Institute of Critical and Creative Writing has shown me first-hand how the 'teaching' of writing is done, and with what results. I am conscious of the debates about whether writing can be 'taught', and it's not something I have much of an opinion on, even now. But I do know that it can be shared, and developed, and brought to a stage of presentability by means of a process that looks a lot like learning. This is because, though having something to say is a state, writing is a skill. This is both good and bad: good because it can be honed and improved with practice, and bad because it's work (and often feels like it too).

The most valuable part of the creative writing course is the group discussion, and the sense, as we go, that we're building towards something shared – however much the results may be individual. The students put a great deal of effort into each other's work: commenting, suggesting improvements, tweaking a voice here or a turn of phrase there. Sometimes the suggestions are dramatic, and the criticism direct. What saves them, I hope, from offending is the care with which they're given and the usefulness of the offered remedy. Sometimes the remedy is simply: 'drop it – try something else'. But knowing when to stop, knowing when we are engaged in the wrong story or have taken on the wrong subject, is as useful as knowing how to keep going. One way in which group work can help us to think outside our own parameters is to help us ask not 'what is a poem/story/novel', but 'what can a poem/story/novel *be*'.

This anthology testifies to the range of approaches in Birmingham City University's creative writing programme. We'll find not just the expected genres, but also writing that crosses genres, that refuses to be straitjacketed by a form that pre-exists it. It's vivid, thoughtful, allusive and direct, but never less than representative of the healthy group ethos of readers and writers who know that if they're alone, they're at least alone together.

Patrick McGuinness
May 2015

alone together

BIRMINGHAM CITY
University

Charlotte McDermott

In September 2011, Charlotte Louise McDermott began her BA studies in English and Creative writing in the hopes of becoming a novelist and poet. In 2014 she achieved her Degree, going onto study her Masters in Writing, whilst she maintains her online presence under the pseudonym Cyanthian. She worked as a magazine editor, *Treeline*, as part of the International Society of Arboriculture, from 2012 to 2014. Charlotte's first book of poetry, *Branches*, is available through Issuu.

Stories Don't Grow on Trees

Let's write a book about the places we've been,
A sort of travel diary or work of non-
Fiction, fleeting moments of adventure,
Endeavours, places that were previously
Unseen or unheard of, places of romance
Or tragedy or history or architecture or
Natural wonder, that leave me wondering
Why and how we came so far in little time.
I'll write the first paragraph, you read it back:
El Tiede rises and falls in around the vapour,
With clouds rolling over the hills as we
Drove through them, clouds, ash clouds,
Lava streams, rivers and seas, obsidian scarring
The land, but trees still grow, and plants,
And the sun shines between the shade,
A rainbow forms amidst the clouds
Upon the wastelands, the volcanic lands,
Lands filled with tragedy and history
And natural wonder, and it makes me wonder
Whether people lived and died here,
Fought for their lives and cried here,
Or was it always barren, silent under the
Mountain, the volcano; how long did it take
For the trees to dare to grow back?
What good is a journey that nobody sees?
What good is a book that nobody reads?
What good is a love that doesn't last forever?
Can it teach you a lesson, can it make you

Wiser, smarter, better? The trip is over.
I will rip the pages from the spinal crease
And let them scatter in the wind like leaves,
Falling from branches of wasteland trees.

En Los Gigantes

I was only ten years old, feels like a lifetime ago,
When I walked into those closed patio doors, leaving
A greasy face-print on the otherwise unmarked pane;
The window held a fraction of my image for a week,
Until I couldn't take it any more and smeared
The forehead, nose, lips and chin across the glass,
So that my father could no longer point and laugh.
Eleven years later I still think about the sliding
Door that tricked me into thinking it was open,
So I could walk right through and leave a mark that
Nobody else could see; these days, when I press
My features against windows, or even mirrors
So I see myself doing it, I wonder why the effects
Last longer than we do, like our breath on glass.

Insect

Dance, Iris, dance, rock from side-to-side
To the rhythm of the wind hissing, like a threat display,
Through the reeds along the riverbank; pray, pray,
Praying mantis, mantes, mantises, sway in unison,
Like the reeds along the riverbank; camouflage,
Greens, pinks and yellows mingle in petals and insect
Bodies swaying, spreading wings with mouths agape,
Smiling when they mimic the leaves; prey, prey,
Praying mantis.

Grigori

Repent, and thou shalt be saved;
I repent, but nothing has changed.
The Irin, for the beautiful daughters of man,
Have fallen from that high Heaven,
The Fifth, the final, the fallen.
The Creator is forever silent
As the pen that does not write;
Penemue taught the humans how to scrawl,
Now the humans do not need us any more,
So what good are we as Watchers without wings?
We were the heroes of old and the men of renown,
But Uriel now, she speaks to Noah
As The Creator shall wash away our sins,
Cleanse the world with waters and let it drown;
What good are we as angels without wings?
We cannot fly and leave these storms behind,
We cannot leave the world unseen,
We cannot change the past, the flow of time;
Been and gone the pleasures of the Earth,
Allow me peace to rest and take me home.

Alex Apati

To talk about Alex Apati in fifty words is a challenge. This is not because of the complexity of his lifestyle, balancing education and work whilst trying to pursue a career in comedy writing - instead it's because he simply hasn't done anything. Nothing at all. In twenty years. Nothing.

A Spare Ticket

My mirror is a window frame. Emma said that this was a good sentence. She said that it says more than just the six words that you have to read. This means that it has another meaning. There are twenty two letters (including one capital letter) and a full stop. Emma thinks that it is powerful because it means that when I look in my mirror I do not see myself. Instead I only see everything in front of me. Emma said that it is also a good and powerful sentence because it says something about how I feel now, because I am not able to look at myself for one reason or another. But then she also said that it has a positive connotation. And a connotation is something what reminds you of something else. And she said that this has a positive connotation because if all I can see is what is in front of me then it means I am looking to the future and not to the past no more. Emma said I should write things down as a story because I am creative and I have a tension to detail (I think). For example, I know how to hold my breath for exactly one hundred and twenty seconds because I play the first one hundred and twenty seconds of my favourite song in my head.

Emma said that a tension to detail is one of the most important things for a storyteller or a writer to ever have. And I can paint a clear picture into anybody's head even if they've never even seen it. For example; there are a lot of people in here now. Twenty three are in my eyesight and my peripheral vision, but there are also some behind me and some further in front of me and in fact I feel like I am on a stage because everybody is around me. There is a man what is holding a baby but it is not his baby because he is an older man and so it will probably be his grandchild. To my left there are two boys sat with a girl and she's not even waiting for another girl and I know this because her coat is around the back of the empty chair and there are only three glasses on the table. There were five glasses and a plastic bottle on the table but the two glasses and the plastic bottle were taken away. The walls have a lot of pictures on them and to my right there is a bookshelf on the wall but nobody is reading anything and the books might not even be books but you can't go and look because they are neatly piled. But they are not piled in colour order and so I want to go to the bookshelf and pile them up in colour order but I am not allowed to because this is not my building and those are not my books. I am in a pub and I am in a pub because Emma told me not to stay indoors no more. My ex-friend Dan said that I am a loner and I think that it is your fault that he said this, and so in case Dan is right, Emma said I should do socialising. Socialising is what you get when a group of two or more people talk to each other about things that you do not need to know, although Emma said that when you socialise, sometimes you learn things you did not know before. Once I was doing a socialise and somebody said that dolphins are the only animals other than humans what do sex for pleasure. I do not think that this is true because how does somebody know that a dolphin is doing sex for pleasure? A male dolphin might want to have a baby with a female dolphin and so they would do sex but if he couldn't have baby dolphins and that was the dolphin that the scientists used in the experiment then the results would be false and so you would never know.

The saddest thing what I miss is your hand. I do not know what to do with my hand now because it is not holding your hand. You never even had the nicest hands I've ever seen but now I can't see them they're the best hands again. I am not sure where my hands can go either, because my phone is in my left jean pocket and my wallet is in my right jean pocket and my left leather glove is in my left coat pocket and my right leather glove is in my right coat pocket and so there is not any room for my hands to go anywhere or do anything. Emma said that it's not the end of the world, but then she would say that to me. Emma would never say that I'm silly or a fool or an idiot and so she has to be nice and make sure I'm okay. She said I should try and hold somebody else's hand but yours are good because yours are chubby but not chunky and so they were nice and I don't know what anybody else's hands are like because I can't ask people that question – not even when I do socialising.

Emma said I should write this like a letter even though you're never going to read it. I asked Emma if I could write it like a text but she said I should be more formal. And formal is when you aren't friendly, but you aren't rude either. She said I have to write and play pretend that you are going to read it, because that way I can talk about how I feel and what I think right now when really what I think right now *is that how many ants would it take to lift a pork scratching?* And I think it would take more than one family. Emma said that once I am finished with my story-letter she would like to read it and so when I am ready I will let her read it.

I used to wake up when my alarm started to ring at 8am on a morning, except for on a Sunday when I would change it so it would ring at 8:15am so that I could have a lie in. Then I would get out of bed and do a number 2 and a number 1 while I was still sat down and sometimes you could hear the number 1 hit the number 2 instead of hitting the bowl of water already in the toilet. Then I would wash and dry my hands and clean my teeth and splash cold water on my head to wake my brain up. Then I would take off my clothes and be naked in the shower and sometimes I would do things like pretend the drops of water coming from the showerhead were really little spiders and my body would shiver and so I would turn and let the water hit my face and forget about the spiders.

I would then get changed.

Monday is my best day for getting changed because it is 'Freedom Day' and I call it 'Freedom Day' because it means I can wear my clothes and not ever have to think about what colour clothes I am wearing until Tuesday. Thursday is my worst day because I don't like the colour grey anymore. Sunday is a good day because I get to choose my clothes for Monday. There was one day what was the worst day what I ever had because your mother died and it was her funeral and it was on a Friday and Friday is 'Blue Day' except for this day because I had to wear a black suit and I was not being me and my head pounded and you felt when my heart was doing a thing where it kept beating and throbbing because it was 'Blue Day' but then you got me a blue flower for me to give to your dead mother and you cried and then I cried and then in order, your grandmother, your sister, your mother's friend Amanda, your father, and then finally your older brother all did a cry around me and you in the bit where all the flowers were. Then I would have breakfast.

Then I would see you.

Then we would do something. For example we would go to the park and sit on the grass or we would go to the pictures on a Wednesday because it was two tickets for the price of one ticket and so we would buy our sweets before we went to the pictures and you would put them at the bottom of your bag underneath your phone and your inhaler and your tampons.

Then I would walk you back to your house unless I was cold because the pictures was far from your house and so we would both walk back home to my home until you were warm again and then my father would take you home and while he took you home I would do one more number 2 and then clean my teeth and splash warm water over my head to close my brain and then take off my clothes and then be naked. And then I'd put my dressing gown on and go to bed and my father would come home and when I heard my garage door close I would go to sleep because that means that you were safe and okay and happy.

Except now I do not know that you are safe and okay and happy no more because you said that I cannot ask this. When you said I could not ask this I first told Emma and then I did not tell anybody else and this is because I was crying and crying is the third worst thing in the world. The first worst thing in the world is all the wars and the second is when people are suffering but not in wars. And then it was Wednesday and so I needed to go to the pictures because it is two tickets for the price of one ticket. I did ask Emma if she would go to the pictures with me but she has a husband and a child. I asked Emma if the husband would go to the pictures with me but she said no and finally I asked if her child would go to the pictures with me but she said no for the second time that conversation.

So I got my tickets from the lady who gives you the tickets (not the lady who laughs a lot) and then stood with two tickets. I really wish that I could have kept the other ticket and was allowed to watch the film twice in a row but the lady would not let me do this and so I gave it to a boy who was with a girl and I said:

"Here is a ticket for you."

And then he said:

"We've already got our tickets, it's two for one, mate."

And then I wondered whether I could do a socialise with the boy and the girl, so I asked him if he knew the thing about the dolphins. He said that he had heard of the thing with the dolphins and then the girl laughed and then they both walked off without my ticket.

And now I have a ticket what can't be used no more but I do not want to throw it away and so the lesson I learned is to not do the two tickets for the price of one ticket deal unless you definitely have a person what wants the second ticket.

Then I had to tell mother and father because when I got in to my home they asked where you were. They did not ask before I left my home and so I didn't need to tell them then, but I have never lied and doing a lie never even crossed my mind because mother said that a pure mind is a truthful one, or a truthful mind is a pure one, but it means the same thing.

So I had to say to her where you were. Except I did not know where you were so I just had to say to her what had happened. I told her about the phone call and then the shout that you did and then the crying what I did and then the telling Emma and then what Emma said and then about the pictures with the lady and the ticket and the boy and the girl and then about the film. And she asked me if I was okay. I said no. Then she said that I will do her proud and so now that is my newest job.

I don't think that I am very good at this. I think that it feels like you have died, but you haven't died. I am just not allowed to talk with you anymore. Emma told me not to worry and that there are plenty more fish in the sea, but I don't understand what that means as there are no links between being a human and being a fish and I know this because a mermaid isn't real, and even if there was such a thing as a mermaid, there's no way there would be enough mermaids in the sea for everyone. I know this because the sea is already full, and it has sharks and whales and dolphins which take up the main room but then there are millions of other little fish and some medium fish, not to mention all of the boats. Emma is right about a lot of the things a lot of the time but that doesn't mean she is right about every single thing every single time.

Joe Legge

Joe is the most talented writer of this, or any generation, [CITATION NEEDED] and is frequently published in expensive literary magazines [CITATION NEEDED]. He is widely credited with the invention of the vampire genre and Times New Roman [CITATION NEEDED]. His memoir 'Purple Cucumber' is being adapted for screen with Helen Mirren set to play Joe [CITATION NEEDED]. Joe is secretly married to Emma Watson with whom he has two beautiful daughters and another daughter [CITATION NEEDED].

This year Joe has been influenced by Chuck Palahniuk, Vladimir Nabokov, Alex Apati and Samuel Beckett. He encourages you to read them all.

Eddie's Ghost

If God ever looked down at the Wye Valley he'd see a turtle shell pattern expanding for miles around; various greens parcelled up by a tessellation of disorganised roads and slowly flowing streams. And if God did look down, and put on his glasses, he might be able to make out a house. It stands alone, surrounded by fields and trees, like a lonely barnacle fixed to the giant turtle shell. It's an eighteenth century farmhouse owned by George and Lorraine and enough children to start a volleyball team. Lorraine is Australian in both heredity and temperament, rarely taking anything too seriously; I can't picture her being angry or upset for a second longer than necessary. The oldest son, Eddie, recently turned fifteen. He's athletic and has a precocious sense of humour. He's popular at school and is growing into a good looking young man who, everybody agrees, is destined to break a few hearts. I've known this family for longer than half of them have been alive and on one sunny Saturday, back when Eddie was nine, I spent the day visiting them with my sister, Kezia, who played games with the girls all afternoon as I lifted the boys above my head and threw them down on their trampoline until we were called inside for dinner.

By the time we had finished eating, dark had settled in and Lorraine, Kezia and I were the only ones left sitting around the dining table. George was preparing the younger kids for bed and the older ones were noisily playing a board game in the living room. The large table that had comfortably seated ten of us now looked like the scene of war after the soldiers had left. Towers of plates cast shadows over abandoned cutlery, strewn like body parts across the table top battlefield. Peas littered the chairs and floor like spent bullet casings as gravy congealed like blood and scabbed carrot coins to place mats. Like every visit to George and Lorraine's, dinner was fun.

As I spooned ice cream into my mouth Kezia asked Lorraine if the vast house with its cavernous rooms ever seemed just a little creepy.

"You know," Kezia said, "because George is away a lot."

"Nah." Lorraine reclined in her seat. "Not since all the ghosts disappeared."

Kezia looked at me and I laughed, assuming Lorraine was joking. Hearing her refer to ghosts felt as realistic as her talking about unicorns.

Kezia looked back at Lorraine, "What happened?"

Lorraine raised a surprised eyebrow and turned to me, "You know, don't you?"

I swallowed my ice cream, "No."

A few months earlier I spent a week working for a company that George co-owned. I stayed in Eddie's room and he was relocated to the room shared by two of his younger brothers. At night, when the house was quiet, soft winds sounded like voices whispering and strong winds sounded like a man crying far away.

Lorraine sat up, "I thought I told you." She paused and the asked "When you were here, did you feel anything weird? Maybe in Eddie's room?"

I thought for a moment before answering, "No." Then I refilled my glass of Pepsi.

"You didn't sense," Lorraine leaned forward and we copied, "any....presence?"

Half way through my stay the family went on holiday so, for three days, I was alone. And because they only owned children's DVDs, and I had no phone signal, and their house is miles from anything, I occupied my time by exploring the house's many nooks and crannies, and playing Killers songs on the piano. I climbed the beams of the tumbledown barn that stood next to the house. I built a dinosaur out of Lego.

I had looked through drawers and bookshelves hoping for something to entertain myself. With no respect for their privacy or secrets I tried to search every room for entertainment or distraction but there was one door that, although it wasn't locked, I couldn't open. I couldn't even touch it.

The cellar door was only four feet tall; made of vertical planks of charcoal coloured wood that were spaced just far enough apart to permit a sinister hand to extend skeletal fingers out of the dust laden blackness and into the real world where children play on trampolines and we throw peas at each other and I make dinosaurs out of Lego.

Unsure how to explain this I just shrugged and asked what happened.

Over a century ago a teenage girl had slept in the room that had become Eddie's. She became sick and died and one night she appeared. She wore a long sleeved nighty and stood in the middle of his bedroom and looked around, stepping silently, turning slowly as if admiring what the new tenants had done with the place. This appearance was the first of many but she never spoke and Eddie never saw her face which was blurry like a victim on the news that had been obscured.

The teenage girl was first and then came others. Lorraine was in Eddie's room reading him to sleep. His room has a door that opens onto his brothers' room and Lorraine looked up from the book to see Eddie staring through it. He didn't blink, and he didn't notice when his mum stopped reading to speak to him.

"Eddie, what is it?"

"There's a man on the end of Felix's bed."

Lorraine jumped up and looked into the boy's room. Felix and Daniel were sound asleep.

"Eddie, there's nothing there."

"Yes there is." He kept staring. "He's holding a funny shaped knife."

Lorraine explained that nobody was there and told Eddie to lie down while she finished the chapter. She read and Eddie fell asleep, and then she looked into the boy's room one more time before switching off the light and went downstairs to tell George what happened.

The next morning Lorraine was in the kitchen and Eddie was at the table drawing a picture. Sat quietly, he was absorbed by his activity, and when Lorraine stood behind him and asked what he was drawing, he jumped a little.

"It's the knife the man was holding."

Lorraine looked at it and saw that he had drawn a sickle. Back when their property was a working farm a sickle might have been a familiar sight.

Lorraine looked at me and Kezia and asked, "How would a nine year old know what a sickle looks like?"

We didn't know but I pictured their cellar, full of dusty antique farm equipment, and wondered if Eddie could have braved the cellar door and gone down to explore. It's possible there were sickles in the cellar but I seriously doubt it.

The ghosts became a constant presence in Eddie's home life. None of them spoke and they rarely even moved. But it came to be that they were always there. Two men hovered a foot above the floor while his family ate breakfast. He opened the bathroom door and found an elderly man sitting in the chair Lorraine used when feeding her youngest. The teenage girl watched him go to sleep and she was the first thing he saw when he woke up every morning.

All of this worried George and Lorraine so they started doing some research. That's how they found out about the girl's death in Eddie's room. They found out about other deaths too, and other hauntings, but they never found any solutions. They looked into child psychologists and considered hypnotherapy. A minister from their church came and spoke to Eddie and said a special prayer intended to protect the house. The word 'exorcism' was mentioned. They talked about moving.

Lorraine started to experience ghostly intrusions too. Every day, after George had gone to work and Lorraine had taken the kids to school, she would stand at the sink and clean the plates and bowls used at breakfast. One day, and then every, she heard footsteps above her, as if someone was walking through the bedrooms upstairs. The sounds were so clear that she could pinpoint where the ghost was stepping. It walked in a long straight line, ignoring doors preferring to move through the walls.

Lorraine ran upstairs and burst into the room but found it empty. The next day she tiptoed, hoping to sneak up on the ghost, but again she found nothing.

"I thought perhaps I could only hear them, but Eddie could see them," she told me and Kezia. The truth was much simpler: after returning from the school run Lorraine would load laundry into the machine. With six kids, there was always laundry. She then went into the kitchen to clear the breakfast table and water clunked through the old farmhouse pipes. Tap, tap, tap, on the way to the washing machine, and Lorraine interpreted the sound as footsteps.

The three of us laughed at Lorraine's paranoia.

"What happened with Eddie in the end?" asked Kezia.

She told us that Eddie used to refuse to be alone in a room because there was always something there and it scared him. Partly this fear came from the way they looked with slightly blue, incomprehensible faces.

"Blue?" I asked.

"Yes." Lorraine smiled. "He started to connect blue things with ghosts. I had to switch bleach because one day he went into the bathroom and saw the blue toilet cleaner and thought the bowl was haunted."

Kezia smiled and shook her head, "Poor kid."

"He used the downstairs bathroom until the bottle was empty and I bought a different one."

Kezia swallowed a mouthful of ice cream. "The one outside?" I'm sure she was picturing the spider webs and dead flies, and the ice cold seat.

"You didn't switch bleach when Eddie got freaked out?" I asked.

"No way! Nothing wrong with that bleach. I'm not wasting it 'cos my kid has the sixth sense." She offered us both another brownie which we accepted.

After a while Eddie stopped being scared and carried on like normal. The ghosts became like an ugly painting on the wall; it may not be very nice but it fades into the background and becomes mundane and no longer noticed. Lorraine asks him about the ghosts every so often and she thinks that they'll all be gone soon. Occasionally Eddie entered a room and would say "Where's the lady gone?" or the little boy, or whoever had disappeared, forgetting that he's the only one who could see them.

The man on Felix's bed only showed up once but the others stayed for a while. The first to appear was the teenage girl, and she was also the first to go. One by one the other ghosts have been showing up less and less, and some have disappeared for good, slinking soundlessly back through the gaps in the cellar door and retreating to the shadows where their blurry faces won't be seen and they handle the sickles and scythes that are lit by nothing but their own milky blue auras.

If God looked down, and put on his glasses, and squinted, he'd see that even with all of this, Eddie is fine. He was nine when he first saw the girl in his room and now he's a teenager. He probably wouldn't mind a nightly visit from a teenage girl.

I asked Lorraine what it will be like in another hundred years, when it's her family's turn to haunt the old house. Her two daughters, Gretchen and Olivia, came into the room so that

Lorraine could settle an argument about whose turn it was to choose a DVD.

Lorraine settled her daughters' quarrel and looked from them back to Kezia and me.

"At least the ghosts we have are quiet. I feel sorry for whoever has us haunting them."

This story is non-fiction and the names have been changed.

Imogen Collins

Imogen grew up in Oxford and moved to Birmingham to study a BA in English and Creative Writing. She is currently in her third year at university and hopes to continue her creativity in the near future by studying at a Masters level to develop her skills further.

Pumpkin

rounded, curvy body
a little bumpy to the touch,
large and plump
you are mine.
I admire you for days,
pick you a name,
run my finger down your back.

The time has come
I take my sharpest knife,
cut you open,
out spill your guts,
cook your flesh,
eat you up.

Prints in the Snow

It's Christmas Eve. I am curled up on our brown leather sofa wrapped up in my mother's red blanket. It smells faintly of Coco Chanel and Indian spices. On the oak coffee table on the far side of the room, sits a wooden bowl of steaming molten red liquid with floating cinnamon sticks and orange slices. The smell of it makes me warm. A plate of mince pies is placed on the pouf, a bite missing from one of them, crumbs gather below it, a pile of rocks deposited at the bottom of a cliff edge. I don't like mince pies. The heavy, emerald green curtains are slightly open, close enough to keep in the warmth but parted enough to see flakes of the first snowfall in years as they flutter onto the already white ground. I glance outside; the snow appears to be stopping. I uncurl my legs and get off the sofa, sliding my feet into my slippers placed neatly on the floor. I go into the kitchen, and pick at a Kalamata olive that sits in a bowl on the glass breakfast bar. The bitter sweet taste teases my palate. Cheesy Christmas songs play on the radio. Mum is preparing to make us all a large steaming pot of curried carrot and butternut squash soup. When she's not looking, I take one of the carrots she's about to use from the chopping board, hide it in my dressing gown pocket and slip out of the kitchen. I bring it with me to the hallway, open the front door and feel the coldness of the night envelop me as I walk a little into our lane. The top of my car is covered by at least three inches of snow. Small flakes land on the side of my cheek, melt in my hair, fall into the gaps in my slippers. I place the carrot near the bushes a couple of yards outside the front door and make my way back inside. I can still taste the olive in my mouth. I wonder if he'll come tonight.

*   *   *

I look out of the car window, the fast straight countryside road on the outskirts of Oxford blurs past me. It's the start of spring, it's foggy and the morning air has a chill to it. Dad is driving. I am eight years old. We are going on a chrysalis hunt. Because of the time of year, he tells me the cabbage white butterfly would be best to look for. "You've just got to look," Dad explains, "they camouflage to protect themselves, so just keep your eyes peeled." He enthusiastically tells me how a chrysalis is once a caterpillar, that once it knows the time is right, it secretes a special silk that hardens when it comes into contact with air. The caterpillar buries itself inside and stays there over the winter, nice and warm in its cocoon, until it knows the weather is becoming warmer and it prepares to break free as a butterfly. It will wait for a couple of hours for the blood to reach its wings until it finally picks up the courage to spread them and fly. It will thrive in its beauty for a maximum of two to six weeks, until it perishes and gets picked up in the wind as dust.

We arrive at the edge of the woodland, my metallic purple wellington boots sink into thick, deep mud. Going into the woods, the leaves swish under our feet, birds sing above us, a rabbit dives into its hole. We make our way along flattened leaves and compacted mud made into a footpath from other walkers. I am excited to look for a chrysalis with my Dad.

At the time, I thought it sounded magical, how something so ordinary and useless like a caterpillar could go to sleep for the winter and become something entirely different, a completely new and beautiful living thing. However, what happened that day could not even come close to how I felt about finding a chrysalis. What happened was something far beyond my greatest expectations and dreams. The moment I saw him for the first time is a moment I will never forget.

I am inspecting a leaf and my dad is doing the same a couple of trees away, when everything around us suddenly becomes silent. The birds in the trees even appear to stop singing. The fog of the morning has now declined to waist height and the early yellow sun is trying to break through the thick grey clouds. In the middle of the clearing between the sycamore trees, no more than ten metres away, I see something from the corner of my eye. I look again, sure to be seeing things, when a large silhouette comes from the clearing, making its way into the woods. I look closer and see a huge figure coming through the mist. My breathing shallows. I daren't move. The dark figure comes a little closer. I look down where the fog on the floor is clearing and I see hooves. Long thin legs, holding up a huge, thick, meaty body covered in a coat of the most gorgeous shade of reddish fur, slightly matted from the dampness of the morning. It is looking straight at me, we make eye contact, but I look away, intimidated and shy. I wonder if he wants to hurt me. He elegantly takes a cautious step in my direction, his dark brown eyes, long thick eyelashes, and the most alarming set of antlers; some of them snapped and scarred.

I had found, or rather, he had found me. My first huge, beautiful stag.

Red deer are the largest land animal in Britain. An adult male can grow as tall as seven feet and weigh as much as thirty stone, more than twice as much as the average human male. Their antlers are extensions of their skulls, velvet in texture and tend to grow symmetrically. Wild deer will often have damaged antlers as a result of fighting off other males to protect themselves and they can live up to eighteen years. Many consider them pests, but not me.

He takes another step, snapping a twig with his sturdy hoof. He sniffs, twitches. I creep forward, but he steps back. I stand still, he steps forward again, then stops. He stares at me. I wonder what he is thinking. He is so close now I feel I could touch him. Two clouds of condensation escape from his nostrils as he exhales. I can see the velvet texture on his antlers. Without warning, he turns around and I notice a deep scar on his thick neck. It must have been a bad cut, for his fur has not grown back over it. He continues to turn slowly and modestly makes his way back into the foggy clearing. I stand there for a few moments, looking into the space where he had been, mouth open, eyes wide. Dad puts his hand on my shoulder, making me jump. He's carefully holding a broken twig, with a single green leaf and a small crinkled object hanging from it. "Now that beats seeing a chrysalis."

Coming home that day, I couldn't stop thinking about the stag. I had never seen a creature so magical in my whole eight years of life. I needed to see him again. I begged my dad to take me back to the woodland every weekend for months after. We took the ten minute drive, traipsed through the woodland, up to the clearing and often beyond it, but to no avail, I never saw my stag. When my sister passed her driving test, it was the first place I asked her to take me. When I hadn't seen him for a long while, I started to worry about him. I dreamt about him most nights. I told my friends and teachers about him, and even won a prize for writing a story about him. Before I knew it, two years had passed and still he had not returned to me. And then one day, I saw him.

He had found me. I was sitting in my living room, watching something on TV after school, when I happened to glance out of the window. In front of our house, beyond the lane is a small woodland area, surrounded by fields. It was autumn, the evening had begun to draw in. The sun, low in the sky, burned golden orange through the branches of the trees as the sky turned red... Suddenly, a dash of brown caught my eye. At first I thought a horse had escaped from one of the fields. Then I saw antlers, and noticed the brown fur had a reddish tinge. He twisted his thick neck to the side, showing off his old scar, letting me know it was him. It couldn't be. How did he find me, right outside my home, from the woods at which we first met? I ran to the front door, dying to get a closer look, but by the time I got into the lane he had already turned around. I could do nothing but watch as his large frame walked away into the distance beyond the thick shrubs and trees. It was years before we saw each other again.

Time went by, and so I grew up. Assuming he had forgotten me, I started to forget about him too. I stopped thinking of him, I stopped going to the woods to try and see him, I stopped spending hours drawing pictures of him and I also stopped cursing my family whenever they ate venison for dinner. Then, once again, he came back into my life. This time, I was a teenager. I was in my first year at college and for my photography A Level I decided to venture into the woods near my house to take some shots for my upcoming nature project. I woke up very early one Saturday morning when it was not yet light outside, armed with my Nikon D40, wearing wellington boots and a thick jumper. As I got to the edge of the woods, the sky had turned purple, morphing into hues of red and pink as the sun began to rise.

I loved being in the woods at this time of year. Bluebells lit up the edges of the footpath, cherry blossoms drifted onto the path and in my hair. Birds chirped and danced, spiders hung from dewy webs which glistened in the morning sun that escaped through the trees. A red kite circled above my head, a flash of blue caught my eye as I saw the rosy blush of a Jay dart past. After taking my photos, and the morning becoming immersed in broad daylight, I took a break on a broken tree stump and flicked through my shots. Then I heard it. A roar, so loud, so uncanny, that I wasn't sure I had imagined it. I stood up, almost dropping my camera. The roar came again. I began to walk in the direction of the noise. It sounded like it had come from the direction of the large field behind the woods, a few minutes' walk away. I went as fast I could, sometimes breaking into a slight jog. I walked through the kissing gates, jumped over the stile, past the stream with the old swinging tyre and finally, I came to a fence at the entrance of the field. There, in front of me, was a group of red deer. A herd of them! I could see at least thirty of them, stood no more than a hundred yards away from me. I kept my movements slow and stayed as quiet as I could, hoping not to startle any of them.

And there was my stag.

He, like royalty, stood up tall in the middle of the pack, looking straight at me. He took a step forward.

His nostrils flared and he huffed outward at me. I wasn't afraid. I beckoned him towards me. "Come on, Stag," I whispered, almost begged him. He kept his distance. That day, I sat on the wooden fence and watched my stag family until I noticed that my stomach was growling and the day was drawing in.

Later that night was when I left my first carrot for him in our lane. I wasn't expecting anything, but I couldn't help staying up at the living room window for most of the night. Of course, I ended up falling asleep, my face stuck to the windowsill.

When I woke up, the carrot was gone.

*   *   *

I am in a bright white enchanted forest. The trees hang low, occasionally dropping a mound of snow onto the ground in response to being unable to cope with the weight. The sun casts diamonds onto everything it touches. Birds tweet. I pick a berry from a bush, put it into my mouth, pleasantly surprised by the sweet taste. A white rabbit with a fluffy tail bounces past me, flicking up snow as it does so. I'm only wearing my pyjamas, I'm barefoot, but I don't feel cold. He is with me. He too is white and I can feel him, right now, alive, breathing, eyes wide, cautious. I gingerly touch his thick, furry mane. There is no scar. I run a finger along his silver velvet antlers. A white doe is nearby, she is shy, she stays close behind him clearly not as confident as he is. He nudges her gently, encourages her to come closer, she allows me to stroke the space between her eyes and I run my fingers down her nose.

I wake up smiling. My room is still dark, but through my blinds I can see day trying to break through. Not even checking the time, I put on my slippers and fluffy dressing gown and run down the hallway, passed the Christmas tree, almost slipping and losing my footing as I do so. I open the door and a cold breeze escapes into the house, enveloping my body. I shiver. I see my reflection in icicles hanging from our gutter, notice my breath in front of my face and a robin perched on the neighbour's fence. I step forward. The carrot is gone. I go further into the lane, hungry for at least a glimpse of him. But he is gone. The only thing he has left me is small, neat, heart shaped prints of his hooves in the snow.

Carmina Andra

Carmina came from Romania almost two years ago and is in her 2nd year of studying English and Creative Writing. She is a housewife, a student, a jewellery maker and maybe a writer... Her passions are reading, hand-crafting, hiking and cooking. Carmina's greatest struggle is writing.

3, 40, Dead

I killed my sister's cat yesterday evening. I cut her open and spread her bowels all over the flowers in the garden. No, I don't feel sorry. She deserved it; my sister, not the cat.

"I saw Clara naked last night." my sister Beth said during breakfast.

"You wouldn't have to see me naked if you would knock at the door before entering!" I replied.

"I knocked, but you didn't hear me. You were making funny noises."

"What kind of noises?" Our father asked. He held the piece of omelette suspended on the tip of the fork, peering at me with cruel eyes.

"Noises." She took a sip of hot chocolate.

"Finish your breakfast; we'll be late for church," I told her.

"What kind of noises?" Mother asked.

"I told you, funny noises."

"Like what?" Father kept questioning her. I wanted the whole thing over, so I stood up and took my plate.

"Sit!" Father exclaimed.

No way could she have heard that! I was silent! Kevin was always gentle when we were at my place. I know I was quiet. Well, up to a point, but even so, how was I supposed to know that she was still awake at that late hour?

"What kind of noises?" Father shouted.

Beth swallowed a mouthful of chocolate and choked with it. She coughed for a few minutes, until her face turned red and her eyes became teary.

"Noises... like you and mum make sometimes."

Father turned towards me.

"In my office, right now!"

He took his Bible from its shelf and entered the office, leaving the door open. I didn't dare follow him. I looked at Mother, but she turned her face away.

They found Kevin at the Scott's farm before lunch. Father had him beaten by his men, to teach him a lesson. These church leaders, 'angels of the city', as they liked to call themselves, were the cruellest men one could imagine; with my father at the top. It didn't matter to them that I loved Kevin. All that mattered at that time was that my father's ego had been bruised, which meant that Kevin would have to suffer the consequences. He was beaten with pitchforks and shovels, then left to agonize in front of the church, in a puddle of tears and blood. I thought of Tim, and then of George. Same story... Yet, they have survived, unlike Kevin. Locked in my room, I tried not to disturb Father with my sobbing. I knew there was nothing I could do when Father came home grinning. He didn't let me out to stay by Kevin; I was only able to hear him groaning in the dust, begging for a glass of water.

During all that time, Beth was practicing for the choir.

'I've got the Joy, Joy, Joy, Joy, Joy, down in my heart!' She kept singing.

I didn't dare cry. I kept staring at him through the window shutter, counting the moments until his death. He died later in the afternoon. It took three hours and forty minutes until his left hand fell lifeless in the puddle next him. His brothers carried his body in a hemp blanket, leaving the stain of his life on the cracked ground.

"You'll pay for this," I whispered.

It was Kevin's family who took the blame for the atrocities that hit our family later that week. The dead cat from the garden, the torn-apart Bible in my father's office, the broken piano, the burnt church... they were all considered poor acts of revenge. I am sure my father will blame them for my death too, when the time shall come.

"Forgive me, Father, for I *will* sin."

Ted Bonham

The 5,122,808,515th person alive on Earth and 80,093,634,401st person to have lived since history begun, renowned beauty and incompetent bio-writer Ted Bonham is James Horrocks, an Inadept of Pataphysics and PhD researcher in English (Creative Writing) at Birmingham City University. Find him very occasionally on Twitter @TedBonham.

An Anatomical Portrait of the Artist formerly Drunk on Shandy

Shall we for ever make new books, as apothecaries make new mixtures, by pouring out of one vessel into another? Are we forever to be twisting and untwisting the same rope?

Laurence Sterne.

Shall we-
Shall we dance?
Through the curtains that our kisses have outworn
To your beauty with a burning violin
With Leonard Cohen to the end of love?

One, two, three, forever?

Let us first consider Pound's binding principle.
We've read nothing new in ever of course,
But there's money to be made here somewhere—
We should put together a proposal for the council
To take on that lucrative new recycling contract,
Or flip cheap property from bank foreclosure auctions,
Or else become involved in the manufacture of a revolutionary
    new drug,
Remaining one step ahead of Government regulation
And the University's own guidance on plagiarism
To provide—for a price of course—a cure
For early onset cryptomnesia.

The key is not to pour your heart out
But to get a spare one cut
Keep it around your neck on a length of string
So you'll never be without access to a liquor cabinet.

Are we forever to be decanting Shakespeare?
Was it the Immortal Bard who called for us
To twist again, like we did last summer?
I don't remember much you know
It's not only the old rope that's unravelling
As we sit methodically pulling things apart,
But there's money to be made here somewhere—
And a limited selection of goods
That can be purchased from the prison store.

Ramon Baharanda

A man walks through life, he looks to the stars. You do not say to him "You look at the wrong stars, the stars are too many, the stars are all the same."

I walk through life, I write. My words are my stars.

How can a star be spelling wrong?

How can a star be repeated of other star?

Maybe I think YOU are all wrong. Maybe I think YOU are too many. Maybe I think YOU are all the same, are all repeated.

DETECTIVE DCI ROCK BROCKTON, DETECTIVE by Ross Broughton

Detective DCI Rock Brockton, detective, brilliant but troubled detective, took a drag on yet another post-coital cigarette as the little missy he'd bagged just hours earlier lay sleeping contentedly, her head on his chest. He'd made this little kitty purr. But Brockton couldn't sleep. This damn case. Some nutjob was out there macheteing members of the public - five in the last two weeks, all of them bakers - and Brockton was the only cop on the force capable of dealing with this shit. The pen pushers down at the Yard - Scotland Yard - couldn't hack it. Oh, they were fine when it came to spanking some chav for slapping his bird around after closing time, but for dealing with the REAL shit no-one but Brockton would do. He'd seen it all in his days – institutionalised as a kid after his own Mother had tried to kill him, and time on the streets. It had all given him an intuitive understanding of the criminal mind that the pen pushers down at the Yard - Scotland Yard - simply couldn't learn in their fancy academies and fancy training, fancy degrees in psychology, sociology, criminology. All that to Brockton was just so much bullshit.

But God damn it, he needed pussy.

He looked at Chardonnay - at least that's what he thinks she was called, but then they hadn't concerned themselves too much with the formalities of introductions, their congress was based more on an instinctive animal magnetism - and decided it was time for someone to make a move. Good times can't last forever... at least not for this chick.

"Chardonnay," he slapped her lightly on her naked ass cheek, and she moaned contentedly, half asleep. He'd made this little kitty purr.

"Chardonnay," he said again, a bit louder than he had done a couple of seconds ago.

"Hmmm?" she purred, waking slowly.

"S'time for you to get up and get gone, I'm 'fraid, babe," and he sounded dead cool when he said it.

"Oh.... I'm sorry... I hope I'm not keeping you from anything important?" She looked at him, helplessly, as if desperate for his approval.

He was used to this. A woman's trick. They flash those lamps at you and expect you to be putty in their hands. But Brockton was putty in no-ones hands, especially not some broad. He smiled to himself and looked away.

"No sweat, babe. But f'you could make a move ASAP, that'd be great for the R-Dog."

He watched as she dressed and made her way to the door, turning towards him before leaving, "Will I see you again soon?"

He smiled to himself. "Yeah, no worries,babe, you havn't seen the last of me."

She opened the door, "Call me... I... I think I.... "

He raised a hand at her, cutting her off before she could make any embarrassing emotional confessions. "Yeah, yeah, I got it. See you soon, babe."

Blushing, she made her way out of his apartment. He stretched out on the bed, satisfied with his mornings 'work', and lit another cigarette. This damn case. Bakers. Why bakers? The press had tagged this dweeb 'The Baker Butcher'. The precision of some of the knife-work suggested someone with a deep knowledge of the human anatomy, or at least very big bits of meat, like a pig or whatever those things are in Rocky when he's training in the warehouse. The modus operandi seemed to be to stab bakers to death. But why bakers? This damn case. It was enough to send any normal cop back to dishing out parking tickets in some leafy suburb, but Brockton fed on this kind of pressure. He needed this angst, this game of cat and mouse, hunter and prey. It kept him alive, alert, vital. He was quite complex.

But God damn it, he needed pussy.

Brockton picked up the phone on the bedside table and punched in a number.

"Hello," purred a little kitty on the other end of the line.

"Madison?... Brockton." He smiled to himself as she let out an excited squeal. He knew the effect he had on women. As a teenager he'd never gone to school, preferring instead to take a book of poetry over to the fields, and he'd always had a different girl with him. Always. Nowadays it wasn't out of the ordinary to bag himself five bitches a week. Got to have a couple of days off, haven't you?

"Listen, babe, why don't you come on over see me for a bit? Make your little kitty purr."

"Oh, Rock... I... I can't... I have work in an hour..."

Someone needed to get their priorities straight.

"Listen, babe, f'you wanna be my girl, you better getcher fine self round here, ASAP!" Brockton demanded, insisted. 'No' was not something he needed to hear right now, not when God damn it he needed pussy.

Madison relented, "Well.... I guess I can be a little late, just this once."

Brockton smiled, "Yeah - that's what I thought. See you in ten."

Brockton put the phone back on the bedside table, lit another cigarette, and stretched out contentedly. A buzz at the door. Brockton pushed the buzzer and looked through his CCTV. Security was paramount for Brockton. Everybody in the world knew he was the best damn cop on the force, and there was no way he was going to maintain his rep with inferior security. It was two of the badges from the Yard - Scotland Yard.

"S'up, dudes?" Asked Brockton.

"Rock... we... we have a problem. Spree killer."

Quick as a flash, Brockton fired back. "Tell me something I don't know!" He had a lightning wit that was renowned across the world. If you're on his side it's nothing to worry about, but if you're on the receiving end then make sure you have the number to a good shrink, because you're going down.

Like this one time, one of the shitmunchers from the Yard – Scotland Yard – thought he was being the big guy for some reason, but this guy wasn't the big guy, Brockton was the big guy, and this so-called 'big guy' needed taking down a couple of pegs. Anyway this 'big guy' had bought some new shoes and a couple of people had said "nice shoes." All of a sudden, he thought he was the big guy just because a couple of people had said he had 'nice shoes.' So anyway this 'big guy' is walking around as if to say, 'yeah I'm the big guy now, I've got nice shoes.' But he wasn't the big guy, Brockton was, and this so-called 'big-guy' needed taking down a couple of pegs.

Luckily, Brockton was on hand for the job.

So Brockton rolls up to this 'big guy' and goes "Let's see those shoes." So this 'big guy' shows Brockton the shoes and, quick as a flash, Brockton puts this shitmuncher 'big guy' on blast with "God – they look pretty gay!" Then he turned on his heels and got the fuck out of there.

That was Brockton's style. A quip and an exit. Razor sharp stuff.

So who's the 'big guy' now?

The dudes at the door piped up, "No.... not the Baker Butcher... we think this is something else." Brockton rolled his eyes, as if to say 'here we go again, leave it to Brockton to clean up the streets,' but he let them in anyway, and they came in.

"S'up, dudes?" asked Brockton, again.

"Rock... we... we have a problem. Spree killer."

"Tell me something I don't know!" Brockton re-used the line to demonstrate how brilliant he was and how quickly his mind functioned. The dudes from the Yard - Scotland Yard - had already told him there was a spree killer, and although at first he thought they were referring to the Baker Butcher, they had told him it was someone else, but still a spree killer, so in effect there were two spree killers on the loose. But Brockton had already deduced that from when they told him that this spree killer was not the first spree killer that Brockton initially thought. Which is why saying "Tell me something I don't know," a second time such a brilliant line.

Pure wit.

Pure Brockton.

"Five deaths in the last two days.... arson jobs, all of them."

"Ok, so some nutjob is out there putting the burn on civilians. Any connections in the cases?"

"Not that we can figure out."

"What about locations?"

"Five different locations - The Chop Shop on the high street, the Gilded Cutlet just off the high street, Steak and Kidney opposite the Gilded Cutlet, the Meat Locker next to the church, and Meat Amazing next to the Chop Shop.

Brockton lit a cigarette and looked amazing as he drew the smoke in and then exhaled, making sure it looked as though he was thinking really, really hard, but also that he didn't need to think really, really hard, because to him it was all too obvious.

"Nothing jumps out at you from those names?"

This pair of deadheads just gawped at Brockton like goldfish would at Chinese algebra.

"Well guys.... all the victims, unless I'm mistak...." What was he saying? *Mistaken*? Brockton?!" ... unless you've given me the wrong facts, are Butchers."

The penny dropped. "Of course!" Said the two deadheads from the Yard – Scotland Yard - "so.... you think.... maybe a connection with the Baker Butcher?"

"Does a bear shit in the woods?"

He had a mind like quicksilver. People talk about mental effort in terms of getting the grey matter working. Well, Brockton's matter wasn't grey, it was silver. Quicksilver. Do they give grey medals for podium finishes in the Olympics? No, they give silver medals.

Not that Brockton would get the silver - he would get the gold. So really he had a mind like quickgold, except 'quickgold' isn't a thing, so he had to say he had a mind like quicksilver, but although his mind was like quicksilver, it was quicksilver made of gold.

The problem with gold, within this context, is that it is heavier than quicksilver, or mercury, to give it its scientific name. It's an altogether more lethargic metal. It's a simple matter of density. Gold, you see, in its liquid state retains the erm... you see the uh weight ratio erm... the ions are all fucked... uhm... ... ...

"The Press on it yet?" asked Detective DCI Rock Brockton, Detective.

"We've had a preliminary press conference... one of the guys from The Times tagged him the.... uh.... the Butcher... uh..."

Jesus Christ! How'd these dumb shits ever get to work at the Yard – Scotland Yard?

"The Butcher Baker, by any chance?"

"Yeah, yeah! That's it," answered either Tweedledee or Tweedledum. Tweedledum and Tweedledumber is more like it with these fucking stupid cunts... or maybe that's too harsh. Brockton sometimes forgot his own brilliance, but that didn't negate the fact that he was just too brilliant for everyone else in the entire world. He was, simply, *better* than all of them.

But God damn it, he needed pussy.

A ring at the door. The dipshits from the Yard – Scotland Yard - knew full well that they were in Brockton's shagpad, that they were lucky to get an audience in here with him whatsoever, as he usually had a strictly 'no dudes' policy. He buzzed up Madison and she walked in.

"Oh my God!" She exclaimed, "have you heard the news? There has been two more murders! A butcher AND a baker. The per... pepre..."

"Perpetrator," corrected Brockton, rolling his eyes at her inferior female brain.

"Well, he butchered the baker and he baked the butcher, but he left a calling card - he took fat from each of the victims, rendered it into a kind of... stick... thing, about 8 or so inches tall, and put it in a candlestick holder with a note saying 'I did it'."

The dipshits from the Yard – Scotland Yard - looked baffled. 'What could it mean?' the expressions on their stupid faces seemed to say, before one of them actually did say it.

"What could it mean?" one of them said.

Brockton rolled his eyes at the bungling trio. Curly, Larry and Moe were like Einstein, Newton and Galileo compared to these three fucking twats.

Brockton, though, was better than all of them. Galileo, forty-one before he 'discovered' the Earth moved around the sun? Newton, forty-three until he learned his own laws of physics? Brockton had learned that shit by the time he was 14. He *read* it in a *BOOK*! Try picking one up next time, Isaac, you dozy fucker.

Dumb shit.

Brockton's law of crime fighting? Kick ass, take names. He'd known that shit from birth.

Brockton was already beginning to piece it all together. He was steeped in literature. He'd read Kierkegaard at the age of five, and had read Ulysses in seven hours. He'd done an Advanced combined Philosophy, Physics, Mathematics and Literature degree, but it had been a disappointment to him, and hadn't fully challenged his brilliant mental capabilities.

He tried to give these feckless dregs a clue. "The butcher, the baker, the...." But they looked at him like goldfish looking at Chinese algebra. Most of the bellends down at the Yard – Scotland Yard - knew nothing about literature. They hadn't read

Kierkegaard at the age of four, or read Ulysses in five hours like he had.

"I think I might know who the perp is." Brockton had recalled, using his brilliant mental recall capabilities, a poem that he recalled reading once when he was reading a book of poems. A short narrative about three tradesmen, probably written by one of the greats . Not that any of the shitbrains from the Yard – Scotland Yard – would know anything about any of the greats of poetry. There's no way any of those dippit twats would have read the book of poems Brockton was recalling reading. Brockton had read Kierkegaard at the age of three, and read Ulysses in twenty minutes. Cunts.

Which reminded him – Pussy!

Brockton sent Laurel and Hardy packing. They were in his shagpad, in flagrant breach of his strict 'no dudes' policy. Perp or no perp, they had to go, especially now his next bit of hole had turned up. These muppets had to get the fuck gone. ASAP!

"Dudes, look. I know there's a killer out there, what say you pair do one, eh?"

And with that, they slunk away, tails between their wretched legs, ashamed to have wasted Brockton's time in such an egregious fashion. Brockton was on this killer thing, but to waste time on that now meant he ain't gon' get no lovin'.

Finally, he was alone with the svelte young thing. This was where he really shone. He removed the fabric lamina that social convention demanded of him until he stood, God like, before his kitty who stood before him like a rabbit standing before the headlights of some kind of unstoppable, unavoidable, oncoming engine powered machine. That is, if you can imagine such a thing, but a rabbit standing before the headlights of some kind of unstoppable, unavoidable, oncoming engine powered machine that had a massive rod on, and was about to fuck it daft.

"Get on it, bitch!"

"Oh, Rock.... I thought we could talk for once."

What da phukk?! Dumb bitch ain't wanna get widdit???

Brockton wasn't misogynistic. How could he hate women - His Mom was one! But Little Miss Queencunt here seemed to think her hole was some kind of national treasure, that she was too good to wrap her flaps around the priapic demi-God standing before her. The engorged head, the pulsing shaft, the glistening tip. The swelling sack, generating seed, the folds of skin. He had a massive rod on, and now cocktease was clamming up?

"Look bitch, you better get on it or get the fuck gone, now! I got bitches lined up. This is your chance."

Anyway then he fucked her. Another one bites the pillow, yeah? Bitch got pinksocked.

"S'time for you to get up and get gone I'm f'raid, babe," he said after he'd dumped his muck.

"Ok.... but..... can I just ask?..."

Jesus Christ! What the fuck was it with bitches and yammering? But he thought he'd let her talk because he wasn't misogynistic. He had a deeply complex and complicated relationship with women. His dad had bailed when he was eight, and he had been raised by his Mom, who he still saw regularly and had a good relationship with, even though the cunt had once tried to kill him and he had to spend time in a fucking mental bin because of it. The cunt. Which is why he couldn't be misogynistic. He'd seen the damage dudes could do when they didn't respect bitches.

"Ok, what is it?"

"Well.... how is it that your renowned for being the best damn cop on the force? I mean forensics can take hours examining a crime scene and then you turn up and seem to be able to immediately solve it?"

Forensics! Bunch of geeks with clipboards and beakers. Hours and hours and hours examining a crime scene for clues, when Brockton could just rock up and immediately understand what kind of guy he was going to end up looking for, because, after all, it was always he that the suits down at the Yard[1] ended up relying on to solve the case because he was the only cop on the force capable of dealing with this shit.

"I guess.... I ... I just seem to have an intuitive understanding of the criminal mind."

"But," said Madison, trying to wrap her head around all that this implied. "You're the hero of this city. This city needs you desperately, because you're the best damn cop on the force, incorruptible, always looking out for the little guy, but not tied down by the bureaucracy of the pen- pushing, desk-sucking, blotter-jotters down at the Yard – Scotland Yard. You have no time for their bullshit. For you results supersede procedural correctness, and you get results, which is why you're so begrudgingly tolerated by that useless shower."

She stopped to reflect on what she'd just said. Yap yap yap.

"I guess what I'm trying to say is, how can it be that someone who performs such incredible work keeping this city safe for the ordinary folk can possibly understand those who are so hell bent on trying to destroy it? How is it that you have such an intuitive understanding of the criminal mind?"

Brockton said nothing. He just lit a cigarette and smiled quietly to himself and looked enigmatically out of the window, but not specifically at anything, just off into the far distance somewhere, as if by looking out so far across the horizon he was somehow looking deep within himself at the same time, which made him look even more enigmatic.

Madison continued, "You're so complex. It's as if there is a darkness to you that you keep suppressed so that you might keep this city safe. Maybe you and the crims you chase aren't so very different, you and they? Your dualistic nature is ultimately what makes you such an intriguing character."

Brockton, saying nothing, lit another cigarette. He took a few

1 Scotland Yard

drags, the folds of smoke folded around his head, and light shone on it from the sunlight outside. He looked enigmatic. Without looking at her he said, "S'time you were gone."

Madison relented. She sighed heavily, collected her things and made her way out, but before leaving she looked back into the room and said, "When will you let someone reach you?"

Brockton said nothing, and with that Madison left.

Anyway then he solved the case. It was the Candlestick maker.

THE END.

John Hunter

John Hunter is a mature student on the MA in Writing programme at Birmingham City University. John has been interested in writing all his life, and enjoys the struggle of trying and make his words mean what he wants them to. John sometimes write under the pseudonym, Jon Wright, and this year he produced a short film, 'Hands', for the Swipeside Film Festival. A copy can be viewed at https://vimeo.com/124087742

BARMAN
(After Bukowski)

I stand at the bar drinking.
(What else would I do?)
You keep them coming. All night long.
It's a job, I suppose - a Barman.
Your tight black pants, hugging your tight white bum, in their
    vice-like grip.
And lower, your strong thick thighs, you use for the dancing.
This game we play, this cat and mouse routine, all night long.
You, standing at the edge of the bar, watching.
Watching in a way I cannot see, so I do not know you are watching.
Surreptitious like.
But I know.
I watch you watching me in your 'I'm not watching you, way.'
Knowing that sooner or later one of us will crack.
Most likely me.
The glass is almost empty now.
You dance around other customers. Eyes averted, but still on
    my glass.
I put it down, empty.
Before it hits the bar you're at the pump.
Pulling me another.
You look over, catch my eye.
"Another?"
Knowing full well, my watching, your watching, has already
    answered your question.
And you're not going to pay for it, are you?
No. Not at all.
After all, you're only the Barman.

Epiphany

The face looked very similar,
To one I had known all my days,
The clothes seemed very familiar,
As he lay there, still, in a daze.

I could not seem to find a name
A name, to match this bloodless face.
My mind contained no link, no trace,
I turned, and looked away in shame.

A crowd began to gather round,
With heavy hearts, and brows and frowns,
And stared in silence, all eyes down,
Upon the figure on the ground.

Though I was looking down on him,
My view seemed somehow to recede,
I felt my body gather speed,
The whole sad scene was growing dim.

Then all I once I realised,
And in that instant, filled with fright.
I knew his name, his cold blue eyes.
I hurtled breathless into light ...

Three Poems for my Mother

1
Sense of Purpose

You had no code to call your own
No other lifestyle had you known,
Only nature drove you on,
Nature, and the norms of home.

You had no purpose, map, or plan.
No goals, apart from: "serve your man".
Your life was simple, circumscribed,
The faithful wife, most loyal bride.

His passing, caused you endless grief,
Death stole your heart, most callous thief.
Alone for years, you struggled on,
Your reason, and your purpose gone.

Your life was simple, straight and true,
Life held no mystery for you.
There was no need to reason why,
But only duty. Do, or die.

2
A fading presence

At six o'clock the phone would always ring,
That precious time, that time which spanned the years,
That special time, when both of us would bring,
A mutual need to pacify our fears.
And thus, through spoken words, we'd both deny,
That standard phrase, that well rehearsed reply,
Those creeping shadows, stalking through the night,
Those careless repetitions, which foretold,
The sad result of merely growing old.
That slow encroaching darkness of your mind,
That vast untraveled plain of pain and fright,
Your journey through a country undefined.
So skilfully you hid, that I'd no clue,
That you had gone, long, long, before I knew.

3
Endings

The sheets were barely moving as I stared,
And listened hard, to hear that hiss of breath,
To indicate that you had chosen life,
And in this hour, had drawn away from death.

So motionless, I think you little cared,
And were not really eager for more strife,
But merely acquiescing to the must,
Of that, still distant pulse, within your breast.
We all, at last, resolve back into dust.

Your ending, came more slowly than I thought,
You sighed, then seemed to lie in silent rest,
While deathly shadows, danced across your brow.
Then, lying back, your final battle fought,
You closed your eyes and looked content, somehow.

Homophobic

The workshop bench, a cluttered heaving mess,
Of laptops, screens, computers, cans of coke:
The air is tense, and words of kindness choke,
Then drown within the chaos and distress.
The youth stands restless, sultry, bitter, bored -
A tightly wound-up fist of rage and threat.
His hard cold lips fellate a cigarette,
Ejaculating smoke, that curls, then soars.

He jerks the laptop's keyboard from its case,
His genes all raging wild, and out of sync,
With all this mundane, senseless, daily grind.
I watch in silence, scan his scowling face,
And see his silent beauty, rise then sink,
Confined within the bias of his mind.

Tim Bancroft

Tim has written numerous articles, shorts and a few books on SF, Fantasy and Historical gaming and is now writing fiction, winning the Orwell Society's inaugural Dystopian Short Fiction award in 2014. He occasionally blogs on writing, life and Pain Management and runs workshops for Writers Reading Aloud.

Etayne Danced for Gryngolet

An alliteration inspired by a study of
Sir Gawain and the Green Knight

The setting sun cast dancing shadows amongst the clitter that topped the tor. Amongst them danced another who was no stranger to the fells. It – he – wondered once more why the granite outcrops stayed stationary. Did they only move when he was not there? He danced and dug to find if they had roots but merely met with yet more rock and seams of solidified blood.

At least, it looked like frozen blood. Was it really once alive?

The dancer flicked his gaze over the haphazard craze of clitter and knarreʒ on the slopes. No matter how long he hid and watched, those scattered stones also never moved, even when encouraged to by pushing them. Perhaps they had merely broken off something much larger, perhaps the towering tors themselves? After all, his own skin shed shards of stone and foetid flakes from time to time. He gently tapped a boulder then his own leg. The sound was the same, that of a hide-clad wose cracking rocks.

That brought another question to the fore. Why did the woses and wodwos have two eyes? And why were the eyes set in an extra limb atop their torso? Such curious peoples.

Perhaps they wondered the same of him: when they first met, the fur-clads seemed so shocked at his lack of such an extra limb that he had set a moss-strewn rock atop his own shoulders in imitation. True, the lichen spreading over it sometimes itched but he now found the boulder's presence comforting, almost a part of him and not just an facade to calm their caution.

If truth were told, he also liked the dance that kept it balanced on his shoulders. Despite its shape, it weaved and wobbled like the woses' limb-with-eyes. His appreciation of them grew: could they, too, enjoy the dance of life?

He had tried to ask but, lately, all ran from him as if frightened. It had not been like that with the fur-clads, many winters ago as they had just run past him on their hunts for the huge-horned oxen that once ranged the fells and forests. And it had not been so with the wool-clads, either: time and again, they seemed pleased that he watched their sheep whilst they went looking for lost lambs. No, he thought, it was the hide-wearers who ran, the diggers who cracked rocks and dug deep ditches into the hillsides in their quest to shatter the solid seams of stone-blood.

A scent: he sniffed the wind.

The chill froze his nose and he sneezed. The slime that stuck to the reeds distracted him from the scent, its sluggish slide along the bright green stem a slow dance of beauty. Was it part of him, still? Did it think? Did it wonder who he was?

He sat back. All these wondrous whys and wherefores never answered: so few replies and fewer resolutions.

Perhaps the knarreʒ were dead – or so slow he would never see one move. Some were etayneʒ like himself, curled up to sleep amidst the creeping cold of winter. He remembered a dance with one in the distant past, though now she rarely woke and he had forgotten where she lay. He suspected some etayneʒ had been destroyed in their sleep by the hide-wearers with their pickaxes, shovels, carts...

...and another thought came to mind, one with anger. Their carts pulled by imprisoned beasts, horses and dogs they trapped and bent to their wicked will. A rage rose in his chest.

Ah, the scent, again. The anger waned. Once more he sniffed and sensed the wind, rejoicing at the myriad variety of odours, their colours and cacophony, their shade and rhyme, harmony and hue. It was a pleasure to scent, to smell, to sample the waves of the wind wending their way towards him. It was easy to become lost in the glory of yet another gift.

Ah. The scent. A horse, a singular stallion, too. Its stink of sweat was warm and rich, an over-riding reek of recent ordure suggesting it was used to dominance, to mastering the minions that meekly mouthed at its manifestation of magnificence. Mmmm...

The horse was labouring under a burden, perhaps, and the wind also brought overtones of tinny oil and tarnished iron.

The etayne rose to wrath, once more. Here was another of the simple creatures slaved to selfish serfdom. He was used to the ponies on the lower slopes of the hills, their simple speech concerned with grass and water and curvaceous mares or strutting stallions. None of their stallions smelt like this, though: none of the moorland ponies ever reeked of raw power.

He imagined the stallion strapped to the front of a cack-wheeled contraption of a cart, dead sticks of wood scoring up its sides, perhaps a bar across its back. He destroyed such prisons whenever he could, grinding and crushing the wood to sticks and splinters, in raw rage ripping them apart. Turned to hobbling nags by their imprisonment, though, the cart-horses invariably fled at his defence of them; they were unused to freedom and struggled to expend the power in muscles crawped up so long.

That they could not dance dismayed him...

...but a hot-blooded horse like this would never succumb, would never allow such ignoble imprisonment. It would shrug such simple straps from its sturdy shoulders, would bite the bridle that dared restrain its royalty. It would be a beast.

Unless.

Unless it was imprisoned by the iron-wearers, the flat-nosed, pale-faced and spindle-spined woses that had ventured into the moors of late. They destroyed the heath, worked the stone, built their buildings, burnt the bushes and crushed the muscles of the land until its heated life-blood oozed from pyres and cairns. He once watched them hammer and heat the hardened sheet to form it into their clothing, a parody of a snail shell's beauty...

...he remembered watching a snail, once, for a whole night. It had slowly slithered its way across a stone to a morsel of moorland mushroom. With an ecstasy of beauty it had entertained and taunted him all through the dusk, darkness and dawn, the spiral wonder of its shell a marvel, a miracle, its alternating striations of colour marching along the twists and turns of its helical home. Its grey-scaled skin, its butter-cream flexible foot (he tried to walk on one foot but had to hop) and the curious stalks on which its eyes danced and swung. He could not now remember where he left it.

There would be others, no doubt.

Ah. A scent. Oh yes. The stallion was nearer now. He could even hear the clattering of its hooves, the harrumph of its voice and the harness jingling. Strange wailings accompanied the noise. He sat up to see.

"Gryngolet, you have ruined my song! Cease your jitters."

He had spooked the stallion. He rumbled an apology that echoed round the hills. In reply the stallion reared, ready to strike with its steel-shod hooves. But he was hidden, the colours of the rocks and lichen blending with that of his skin.

An iron-clad sat upon the enslaved horse. It made a noise like those of its kin. "What is it, Gryngolet? Are there etayneʒ amongst the knareʒ? Wodwos?" The iron-clad's voice rose louder. "Show yourself! Come out from hiding, fell beasts, or if you be mere mortal men, know that you challenge Sir Gawain, Knight of the Round Table, nephew to the King!"

The twittering tones were not unlike the birds whose song the etayne often stopped to hear. The sound was deeper, for sure, but not so deep for speech. The etayne ignored the noises: his concern was for the slave. The stallion was imprisoned, indeed, wrapped with gold-studded leather strapped around its belly, chest and rear. Its face was encased in leather with a solid plate of iron upon its forehead. Straps held the iron-clad's seat in place.

So, how to free the horse?

His gaze was caught by the singular coloured plaque carried by the iron slaver. It was shaped like the end of a large shovel carried by the hide-clad and wool-wearers but was pinned to the slaver's arm. The background was bright red but drawn upon it in a bright, gold line was a five-pointed star. He followed the line under and over itself before it reached the apex of an arm and returned to the centre again. The line never stopped, never ended. There was joy and wonder in tracing such a curious design.

The iron-clad cracked his fascination with a rooky, raucous call. It was filled with the high fluting of fear and frustration. "I am honour-bound to search for the Green Mount, beast. If you do not let me pass, I will challenge you!"

Were the sounds directed at him? He looked around: nothing else answered that he could tell. He listened for more such noises but none came.

"I will free you, horse," he said. His rumbling voice echoed off the rocks around, filled with nuances of freedom. Like others of its kind he'd met, the horse gave no reply. He made a demand of the iron-clad wose. "Release the horse!"

"I take your roar as challenge, O monster of the rocks, etayne most foul." The iron-clad motioned with an arm and a skull of iron snapped down to cover its eyes and mouth. From hoops on the horse's harness the slaver lifted a stick, its point so polished that it flashed gold in the waning sun. The iron-clad forced the horse to turn and trot away. Was it leaving?

No. It stopped and turned to face him, changed its seating and thrust back its heels. Spiked spurs of iron prodded the horse's flanks and the etayne seethed at the slaver's abuse of its steed.

The stallion made no complaint, even seemed to expect the command for it was already surging forward. In moments it was at a charge, heading not towards him but to one side. The iron-clad lowered his wooden stick, leaned forward.

Such strange actions indeed. The horse and its slaver were acting together, as one, seemingly with joint purpose. Was this a dance? Fascination caught him once more and he watched them close, excited to see the speed they achieved in such a short space of time, delighted to see the balancing between them. Such balance matched his with the rock atop his torso. Was his rock a slaver, too?

No time to consider that question: the glisten-tipped stick was going to strike and break. Etayne danced out of the way, the boulder on his shoulders rocking gently. Mere yards from him the iron-clad subtly shifted the stallion's steps so it would shatter again. Did it want the stick broken on his chest?

Quick: maybe once it had done so it would release the horse. He braced himself – for the strike would be at speed – and the stick shattered into splinters. The iron-clad howled as they galloped past him, then slowed to a stop. Would the iron-clad make more sounds?

No. To his delight the demon dismounted. Did this mean it was releasing the stallion? The etayne waited as it pulled a long spike from hoops on the rear of the over-laden horse. It was unloading the enslaved stallion!

"Run, horse, run!" His thundering shout of excitement echoed across the fells. The iron-wearing wose turned its head sharply and called out again, the fear-filled fluting now muffled by the hound-skull of iron. "I hear your challenge, ravager of the fells. Do not fear, I come for you!"

The iron-clad stepped towards him, carrying the strange spike in its hands. Flattened from forged and beaten stone-blood, it tapered to a narrow point at one end with a cross-bar at the other. The slaver gripped it with one iron-clad fist beyond the bar, the other before. The etayne smiled: it was Iron-Bearer now, not just iron-wearer.

Iron-Bearer skipped forward and to one side. It swung his iron spike at surprising speed, first to one side then to the other. His mesmerising motion was acrobatic, awesomely athletic to watch. It was a dance!

The etayne was mesmerised by the magical movement and stood still to watch. The iron spike struck his side with a clash and broke a shard from his skin that fell to the earth and became a stone like all the others. "Time to flee," he called out to the horse. "Time to flee!"

But, despite the distraction, the stallion stood still. Did it need time to realise it could run? He would give it time – he would dance with its master, Iron-Bearer.

Iron-Bearer was speaking. "So you roar with pain, etayne? This is how I deal with your ungodly kind!" Iron-Bearer redoubled his delightful dance, feet flying through complex steps, arms whirling the spike around its head. Etayne was entranced and perhaps that was the aim for the flat-beaten baton battered at the boulder balanced on his torso.

It threatened to tumble.

He tried to roll it back into balance, twisting his torso to one side and another, rocking back and forth with even greater movements as it rolled on his neck. He smiled to himself: he was dancing with Iron-Bearer.

But his companion in the dance whirled its wand once more, striking at the seam. It was beating at his boulder, not doubling in a duet! The strike was too heavy and the rock he had balanced for so many years ripped free from its bright band of restraining moss. The stone tumbled to the floor, rolling before rocking to a halt.

Iron-Bearer stood still. It looked at the rock then back to the etayne.

Etayne stood still, too. He was shocked, his gaze upon the rock that had partnered him in dance for so many years. "I am sorry," he said, though he knew the rock could not hear. He spoke to the still-stationery stallion and his voice was softer, barely a whisper of wind. A plea: "Flee, horse. Flee."

The stallion still stood.

A brisk breeze blew.

Only then did a thought of error enter his mind: the stallion would never escape, its serfdom would never end. The stallion chose a life of servitude. For its constraints, its loss, he began to cry. Great sludge-like tears of streaming mud oozed from his eye and trickled down his chest to slop to the stony soil. He closed his eye.

Iron-Bearer struck with its steel stick once more, the stick clanging and vibrating. "Hist, it bleeds! It roars in pain!"

Etayne sank to the floor on his knees, then folded over with grief. He sobbed as one last strike from the spike smote his back. Footsteps faded away.

"Come Gryngolet, the Green Man calls!" Words washed weakly over the darkening wastes. The stallion, still slave, broke into a clattering trot.

It chose to be in chains.

The noise of the slave and its slaver drifted away: the fells returned to peace.

Etayne rose, rubbed his eye and picked up the boulder that for so long had been almost a part of himself. The rock was undamaged, the lichen and its many hues still safe and the enker green moss intact. He settled it back on his shoulders.

It felt good – no, right – to balance it there once more.

The moon rose over the tors. Again he danced the duel. He imagined the iron-clad's spike swinging, striking and swishing through the air and in the memory and movement lost his melancholy. He stepped and hopped and tripped and twisted and turned and leapt in the air and back to the ground, a moonlit shadow in the darker shadows of the moor. He danced because he could, because he felt as if he should.

Etayne danced for Gryngolet and the life the stallion chose.

Gregory Leadbetter

Gregory Leadbetter is Reader in Literature and Creative Writing at Birmingham City University, where he leads the MA in Writing and the Institute of Creative and Critical Writing. He is a poet, critic and scriptwriter. www.gregoryleadbetter.blogspot.co.uk

Misterioso

Commissioned for Music for Youth June 2014

A shell at my ear,
I heard the whisper of my heart's work:
I fell open like a book.
I watched the quiet of the moth's flight,
drawn to silence like the moth to light:
the life within the one we hear.

Now I am the instrument that I play
and I am played by the sound
I make: remade by the touch of the air,
by the rhythm and note of what I say –
as if the world is something I have found
and the world knows that I am there.

And if the best of speech is music – a sense between
the skin and something understood –
returns the tongue
to its own song –
gives the blood
its dream –

let its language

bring us close
to the first of us: the cave of eyes
lit by the fire of what they heard –

the drum that gives the ghost
its dance: the voice that swells the earth
like fruit: the cry that carries on the listening skies.

Abigail Cooper

Abigail is a second year student going for a BA in English and Creative Writing. She hopes to use this to become a fiction author once she graduates. She enjoys slipping into the minds of the characters she creates and watching them come to life on the pages.

Cold Blooded

I sit curled up in my seat, my hands white and cold, long nails clutch my tattered blue jeans. Sitting between my parents I see neither of them is looking at me. Their attention is diverted from my unnerved state; my mother is reading her book and my father fiddles with his phone. They wouldn't notice if I got out of my seat and slit my throat right in front of their eyes. They still haven't noticed that there's a knife hidden in one of the compartments behind them, that I could easily grab it and push it through their skin like a needle through cotton. It's there because I often wonder if I can use it against someone else. Or if I should make it dance across my own skin to see the crimson blood run down the pallor of my flesh, tainting an innocence as red as blood until it blackens and festers beneath the surface.

I almost laugh at the darkened twist my thoughts have taken on, I wonder if it's wrong to think such things, to hurt someone in a way that could... kill them. I fear where such things come from inside my head. I'm not a killer; the temptation is there to prove that I don't act upon it. The knife is only to defend myself if I have to.

I frown at what would happen if I did give into the attraction, to fight and break out of the trap that has locked me in on all sides. Being trapped in their grasp is turning me to more... murderous thoughts... I wonder if I could actually fulfil such blood-stained fantasies. It would certainly make waiting here more interesting, to get lost in the screams of fear that would fill the room as I stabbed and slashed at everyone in sight, just to see their blood splatter the walls and floor.

The darkness of my thoughts fades for the briefest moment as

I drift back to reality, and swim in the pain and fear that envelops me like a blanket.

I'm not going to fight. I won't spill innocent blood like it's worthless.

But they won't stop... They just won't stop...

I look around helplessly, my arm throbs agonisingly and it shifts with a painful crack only heard to me. Black eyes dart to stare at me, dark and bottomless. I fear I may drown in them as I supress the urge to grab the nearest sharp object to gouge them out just so they will stop staring at me. The owner sits across from me, his hands folded in his lap; his stance is so rigid I think he is made of stone. My thoughts must have been heard because the statue glares at me with eyes that refuse to blink. Silently I turn my gaze away, almost guilty to have thought so openly. I hope he didn't see how much I want to make him scream as I carve out his penetrating eyes, eyes that can see the maddening disease that is threatening to consume my brain.

I wonder for a moment how I may commit the deed, how I can make him cry tears of blood while he screams for mercy and begs me to stop and spare him.

"Stop! Please!"

"You're going to kill me!"

"Please have mercy!"

That certainly is a possibility. But I don't know what mercy is, and if I did, I wouldn't give it. Does it seem like mercy can be given? I don't give mercy, why would I need it? And, carving out his eyeballs would at least ease the boredom. Maybe he won't even be able to speak because he can only scream. That could be interesting.

I push the darkness back again, and instead focus on the room around me, clenching and unclenching my hands in an attempt to curb my bloodlust. I do not know if it works or not.

Everything is white, the seats, the walls; even the lights are blindingly white. It hurts my eyes just to look at them. I squint and rub my eyes to stop the black spots dancing before me. Spotless and clean, there is nothing even remotely dark or dirty. Not even a speck of dust floats in the air, you would think there would be something, but it seems we are trapped in a giant filter. There is nothing in the air but our own breaths. The statue blends in so effortlessly, dressed in a sharp white coat, with silver glasses glinting on the end of his nose. His black hair is scraped back away from his granite like face. The woman next to the stone man smiles serenely at me in her pretty white dress, her belly is engorged, her dainty hands rub circles into the sides. Her happiness twists my insides and I find myself wanting to scowl at her just to make it disappear. Instead, I make my smile as fake as possible, too wide and with too many teeth; she doesn't even notice.

A sweetly sickening scent lingers in the air, it burns the insides of my nose, and I try to stop myself from sneezing just to get rid of it. Why won't they let me go?

Drowning, drowning in a sea of white, why is everything so white? I feel I am the only life in this little world. My red shirt masks my white skin and my brown hair hides my green eyes from the creatures that stare at me so openly. I curl into my seat more tightly. I don't care for the pain that shoots through my arm. I just wish they would stop looking at me.

My mother slaps my knee to make me stop, not once looking up from the pages of her book. I scowl and consider sticking out my tongue just to spite her, but I decide against it, seeing that there is nothing to gain by behaving like a little brat.

Sit up straight. Meet their eyes when someone is speaking to you. Don't talk back. Don't be rude. Be pleasant, polite, and proper. Be a *lady*.

Mother would prefer that I was a good little girl that stayed inside and played with her dolls rather than the tomboy that she got. The reason I ended up in this mess is because I was climbing a tree and fell on my arm. It made this loud snap and I was writhing in agony on the grass that caught me.

"It's your own fault, you stupid girl," she had said on the way here.

Father had driven us up in the silence I had come to associate with him since birth.

I think he finds it easier to stay silent and let Mother take the reins while he goes off and does his own thing. I'd rather like to join him, but I'm stuck under Mother's large thumb. It feels more like a hand though than a thumb, with talons as the bars of my cage and an icy palm as my roof.

A distant drone slurs in my ears and I look up to a smiling woman behind a white desk. Her skin and teeth are a dazzling white, just like her dress; the collar is sticking up so I can't see the curve of her neck. She flicks her hair over her shoulder, reminding me of a plastic doll; she's pretty in her fakery. I don't know why she's got so many people staring at her in awe; she's boring and bland, much like the food I've seen taken around the room and along the corridors, how could they be interested in such a wooden creature?

The smiling lady moves stiffly behind her desk and revives the flowers blooming beside her. I wrinkle my nose. How can she stand them? They have no colour, no scent. They do nothing but sit and watch the creatures pass by, dragging their metal friends behind them by their chains. Are they prisoners I wonder, like I'm going to be? It doesn't look like much fun, dragging the metal aliens around. Are they meant to be their wardens? Because the fact that there's hardly a person I've seen without them makes me think that they are the guards of this terrible place.

I'd like to smash the metal to bits, would my chair be strong enough to do that, or will I need something heavier? I'd love to see how mangled I could make them. But why stop there when I can move onto the creatures?

Bruises turning puce and bulging with blinding burgundy.

Blood splattered like paint on a canvas and awaiting their maestro to finish the masterpiece. Bones cracking, snapping, breaking under just the right amount of force. With screams of terror, of blood, of stone cold murder twisted into sick pleasure...

I drag myself away from the abyss that is the murderous darkness clouding my mind. It seems to be getting worse and worse the longer I wait here.

A glint of silver catches my eye. I dare to look up and smile at the sight of colourful liquid, but my lips quickly curve down. The intense colour that was a beacon in this black and white world has disappeared into the white arm of a small child. Its shiny blue eyes are rimmed with red, painfully swollen with unshed tears. From a thin silver wand the rainbow of colour fades with a push of the plunder, which spills a drop of scarlet onto the immaculate floor before it is swept away. I watch wordlessly as the creature pats the child on its blonde head as its eyes roll back and its head lolls onto its shoulder. A whimper falls from its lips before it fall into the world of dreams.

An uncertainty fills me, whether I should feel the need to empathise with the small child and its pain, or simply ignore it and focus on my own agony. Desperation is the only way I can describe an attempt to flee what is inevitable.

The creature that caused the child to drift away into a realm of sleep fleetingly walks away, giving me a toothy smile that is reminiscent of a wolf's snarl as it passes.

"You'll be next, little one."

You'll be next.

You'll be next.

Must they say such things? It makes my skin crawl, the way they speak to me as if I am a child; it is patronising and degrading, and I am not a child, even though I still live with my parents. I may look like a child, but my mind is faster than they think. I can see what is happening around me as metal monsters skitter behind their prisoners and liquids are used to send their victims into a blissful oblivion, if it can be called that.

They speak as if they plan to kill me, or at least knock me out with the colourful fluid like they did with the small child. I don't want to be next. I don't want to be here. I want to get out of this asylum of lunatics while I still have my sense of self. They want to turn me into a blank canvas like everyone else here. Mother would certainly be pleased, it would make me more pliant to her wishes, and that is something I have no wish to be a part of. She's so distracted by her book, I wonder if I can sneak past her and Father and get the knife from the car...

I push those thoughts away, instead looking up at the ceiling as if it had all of the answers.

The white is blurring now in front of my eyes. I fear I'm going blind. Desperately I blink and rub my eyes with the backs of my hands, black eyelashes sticking into the wrong places to make water spring up from their crevices. It hurts, it's too bright. My insides writhe and scream under its scrutiny, it feels like I'm melting. My inner cries fall as inaudible whimpers from my lips, as silent as the grave to everyone around me, but loud and painful to my own ears.

Stop the burning!

Stop the burning!

I groan in irritation. Why won't they just let me go? There's nothing wrong with me! I don't want that liquid inside me! I don't want to sleep; I want to get out before they completely reprogram me. I'm not helpless. I refuse to be helpless.

Turning my head away from the white lady at the desk with her flat flowers and plastic smile, I glance over at a gaping chasm opposite. My lips pucker in curiosity; I wonder what's through there, what instruments of torture lie behind those closed doors. My legs tingle at the thought of walking away, of escaping and going through the doors to freedom, but my mother's hand on my shoulder keeps me in place.

"Stay still. You'll make it worse," she whispers to me before turning back to her book. "I want to leave as much as you do. Maybe next time you'll think about climbing that tree and breaking something else. Let's hope it isn't your neck."

Worse? How can things get any worse? I am perfectly fine and they have trapped me here against my will. I am a prisoner of their words and hands.

I really wish I could snap your neck, Mother dearest. Maybe then you will see that you can't control me.

My eyes flick back to the white woman again. I wonder if they'd notice me get up and turn this asylum red... They would be screaming in fear, my body splattered with their blood, my hair saturated with it and clinging to my face like tentacles to its prey. Such a sweet masterpiece, to be dripping in a sea of scarlet and to listen to the terror that I have created; if only I could get back to the car and grab the knife so that I could begin my work...

My name is soon called. My thoughts of blood and murder flee back into the darkened corners of my mind, not daring to tread where they fear that they will be caught and captured. It is a reprieve to get away and allow myself to be guided out of the room.

Nabiyah Saddique

Nabiyah, 20 years of age, studying English BA and working towards being the author of a novel very soon. She also wishes to fly in the sky one day. Nabiyah writes for her personal blog at www.cavegirlwrites.wordpress.com and on Instagram at www.instagram.com/nabiyah_.

Hazy Perception

I am confined in darkness. Trapped beneath the scrap of fabric that covers my vision. The rustling of paper catches my attention. Paper? Or maybe a packet. I can't really figure it out. His footsteps are heavy and the floor creaks under his weight. The sounds become louder and louder and suddenly the blind spots that surround me are filled with light; blinding light. After that, everything happens so fast. Suddenly I'm on the ground with something heavy leering above me. Someone. His weight presses against me.

I'm drowning. I fight for every breath, expanding my lungs trying to get as much air in as possible. I open my eyes.

I am in a bed in a room with a white ceiling. I wonder how I got here. I'm shaking uncontrollably and the sound of beeping fills the air. People rush into the room. White coats are all I see before I'm drowning again.

Caught in an abyss, floating from one place to another. Flittering through moments. I wake up in one moment and in the next I'm sinking again. I feel fragmented. As if pieces of me are flying around and I can't even find the energy to catch them.

The sound of murmuring wakes me; people surround the bed I'm lying in. A man with black rimmed glasses is staring right at me. His mouth is moving but the sound doesn't reach my ears. The haze that fills my head refuses to let go. I cannot escape it.

Someone is shaking me but I don't want to open my eyes to the light again. It hurts. All that fills my vision is his face. The man with the black rimmed glasses. He is so close I can feel his breath touch my face. I shake and the bed creaks beneath me. He withdraws and straightens up.

"Hello, I am Doctor Evans. I have been treating you for the last five days. How are you feeling?"

I open my mouth to speak but all that comes out is a croak. I have forgotten how to speak. I try again.

"Where am I?"

My voice is scratchy and high pitched. This doesn't sound like me.

"You are in White Bird hospital. You are safe."

His words resonate deep inside me. I need to know more. I wonder if he can read my thoughts.

"You were rescued by a man called Spencer."

Spencer? I don't think I know a Spencer.

"You don't know him; that is what he has told us. He brought you here after finding you lying unconscious by the river in Southside. We have done various tests and scans to find out exactly what has happened to you. We have found evidence which suggests that you have been sexually assaulted."

The words falling out of the doctor's mouth don't reach my ears. I grasp the white linen bed sheet. My fingers falling into the holes that it is made of. Sexually assaulted. I was raped. Why can't I remember it? My stomach tightens at the mention of rape.

"You may not remember. You have been in and out of consciousness for the past few days..."

The sound of my heavy, rapid breaths fills my ears. I need to focus. The doctor is still talking as I can see his mouth moving but I only hear soft murmurs. I concentrate on his face and I catch the last few sentences.

"..Spencer has been waiting for your recovery. He would like to meet you. Would you like me to call him in?"

I don't know if I do.

I wonder why a stranger would wait for my recovery. I don't know whether to be flattered or frightened. I realise that the doctor is waiting for me to give him an answer.

I nod.

A few minutes later, a broad shouldered man staggers into the room.

"Hello, I'm Spencer."

His voice is deep. He sounds familiar. He looks around warily. "Are you ok?"

He is staring at me expectantly.

I nod.

"I just needed to know that you are alright."

I stare at him for longer than I should, not knowing how to respond. Tears begin to pool in my eyes and spill across my cheek. He looks at me, unsettled, and walks out of the room, leaving me confused.

So much has happened that I am unable to recall. I attempt to get up but fall back onto the bed. It seems all my strength has disappeared from my limbs. I need to do something to stop myself from falling again. I reach out to the bedside drawer and the door swings open. The man with the black rimmed glasses. He examines me from head to toe. I feel uncomfortable under his excruciating gaze.

"Where are you going?"

"I just need to walk for a while."

He walks away leaving me standing at the doorstep.

I sit on a wooden bench and stare at the rose bushes. I pick one of the white roses. Blood trails down my finger. I remember rushing home from work and then recalling that I had left my phone at the bar so I walked back. It was dark. The streetlights weren't working so the only source of light was the moon peeking through the clouds.

I stare at the blood trailing down my finger.

Darkness. A blindfold. A man. Two men. I only heard their voices. The deep voice that sounded familiar. Spencer. I remember his voice. He was there. I sit and stare at the perfect white roses. I notice a speck of dirt covering each of the perfect white roses.

Cheryl Kaye

Cheryl is a writer based in the Midlands. She always loved writing stories, and started writing erotica as part of a journey to re-find herself. Her first published story appears in the anthology, *Tie Me Up* which came out in April 2015.

Destruction

She runs past
Over, around my feet

Boiling, tranquil
Warm and light
Turbulent, peaceful
Cold and dark

With great ease
Smashing man's structures
Smoothing stone
Shattering wood

My pillar, my life
My constant

I've seen her take
My brothers
Sisters, friends
But not me
Not yet, my
Roots too deep
But slowly
She works away

Deep below the soil
Steadily changing
And someday I know
She will also take me

I have spent forever
All alone, waiting
For my turn to come
Watching silently

Desolate
The end is welcome

Needed release
Craving comfort
It's with relief
I will go

I will fall
And my body
Will be taken
Crashed, dashed, broken

Held in her embrace
To my end

Comfort

We're lying together on the bed, fully clothed, on top of the covers. I'm tucked against your body, your chin resting on the top of my head. Your arm is around me, wrapping across my stomach holding me close, your leg is bent over mine, cocooning me. I've been crying for thirty minutes, we've been lying here for twenty, every so often I feel your other hand stroke my hair as you kiss my head. You don't say anything. You just hold me. Knowing you came over when I said don't, knowing you stayed when I fell apart, knowing you just knew, it all helps.

It had been a year since my Dad died. I went to the crematorium to lay a rose for him. I didn't want you to come with me, wasn't sure how I'd be. We hadn't been together that long and you told me you don't cope well with crying women. I had done OK. I got off the bus and walked up the drive to the Remembrance Garden. It's so beautiful there, not to mention how quiet and peaceful it is considering its proximity to the Ring Road. I sat on a bench by the lawn; the scent of the roses in the bed behind the bench filled the air. The last time I was here was for my mum's birthday. It was all bluebells, snowdrops, crocuses and daffo-dils; they looked pretty but there was no scent. Now the scent was heavy, surrounding me. I thought about how my dad was with my mum now. They were together and I was here alone. I'll admit to a few tears at that thought, nothing major though. I'd stopped crying and was in that quiet thoughtful place when I got on the bus home.

I let myself into the building and slowly walked upstairs to my flat, the loneliness filling my chest made it hard to breathe, hard to think of anything else. So when I opened the door to find you waiting for me, you hugged me and it was like someone flicked a switch in my head. The tears started, and they weren't quiet reserved teardrops. They were loud, messy, uncontrollable sobs. You were still in your work clothes and I quickly managed to make a wet patch on your shirt. I had my arms around your waist holding you tight, with my face buried against your chest as I sobbed. You didn't run or panic, you just stood there holding me. Your chin resting on the top of my head, your hands stroking my back. A firm pressure as you moved your hand down from the skin of my neck, to the cotton of my vest. The movement repeated downwards as I continued sobbing. And when I didn't stop, you walked me to the bed, sat me down on the edge and carefully removed my sandals. You moved me onto the bed so you could lie down with me, you slipped two pillows under our heads, and curled yourself behind me, pulling me back against you. You just held me.

When the tears finally stopped, you didn't move or speak, you just continued holding me. Your breathing was so relaxed, I even wondered if you had fallen asleep until you stroked my hair again. I gradually got my breathing back under control, only an occasional gasp escaped as I tried to regain my composure. I leaned back against you, felt the rise and fall of your chest as you breathed, matching my breathing to yours until finally, I am relaxed.

As I calm down I find myself stroking your arm over and over, moving my fingers in little circles, drawing swirls and patterns. And as I keep stroking I notice you stiffening, pressing against me, and I realise I need this. I want to feel alive. I roll onto my back and lean to kiss you, running my hand down your arm, onto your hip and reaching back to grab your arse. I pull myself against you as I bite your lip. The loose cotton of my skirt flares and your hand gropes under it, moving my knickers to one side, while my hands fumble at your fly. Releasing you, I work my hand up and down matching your rhythm but I want more. I need more. I look into your eyes and ask "Please?" You kiss me. As you move on top of me, I reach a hand down guiding you in, folding my legs around your arse, lifting my hips to meet you, pulling you in deeper. I let the rhythm move me to the edge and back again, tightening myself around you, letting it build until the feeling pushes me over the edge. You roll to the side and I cling-on, holding you inside me. Feeling the comfort you bring.

Arif Rahman

Arif is from Birmingham and is currently a first year undergraduate studying Creative Writing with English at Birmingham City University. With a zealous passion for the Gothic and Romanticism, Arif continues to progress and elevate his passion for writing by actively writing and reading short stories and poetry.

Ambiguity

She is ambiguity
There is always one more chapter
Lurking before her pages end.
In her noble novel
She verbally fences the reader,
But then she instills serenity and
Unapologetically drowns tranquility into Jealousy.

I read her with precision.
The imagery of her words soothes my mind.
Misinterpretation is defeated by the
Impossibility of reading her backwards.
She possesses bounteous orthography
That is as magnificent as
The sun on a Sunday afternoon.

The nature of her interrogative in love
Is written in her blood.
Her exclamatives screech poniards.
She will salvage an amorous approacher
And convert him into a sinful transgressor.
I am addicted to deciphering her,
For she is, the sweetest drug.
Her story dictates broken hearts,
Reminiscences and forgotten remembrances

Her heart is imprisoned inside her ribs.
Beauty and love have deceived her

Into a world where tears and darkness share a romantic
   relationship.
She is situated in a land where
Evil serves as the governor,
Inhabited by the many children
Of blithe and sadness.

Vanessa Courtney

Vanessa Courtney is a twenty something writer from Stratford upon Avon, currently studying for an MA in Writing. Vanessa dreams of a better world; a world where she is a famous writer, has exceptionally good hair and where people can spell her name right without a second thought.

Gluttony

I used to take my dreams for granted; I think we all do until we notice we aren't dreaming anymore. I don't dream because I don't sleep, it's hard to sleep when you're the size I am. I'm twenty six stone; I'm probably bigger than anyone you know. I am not ashamed of my size, I know how I got here and I would do it again in a heartbeat if I could, but I have to try. I have to try and make myself someone new on the outside so I can make something new on the inside; Sean wants a baby. I've decided that being pregnant is like being a human kinder egg, inside each woman is a tiny little yellow pod with pieces that can fit together and make something beautiful. The only difference between a human baby and a kinder egg toy is that the toy comes with an instruction sheet on how to put it together and make it work properly, humans don't get that luxury with a baby. Sean and I can't conceive naturally because of my weight. The doctors told us that if I did manage to get pregnant that I would almost certainly lose the baby. It's not as if it would be my house keys, or a cube of Cadbury's. I lose those all the time; they get pushed down the back of the sofa, or melt into my jumper, but I wouldn't lose my baby. I'm not completely incompetent.

I have to sleep alone at night because our king size water bed can only just accommodate me, so Sean has to sleep on a camp bed in the corner of our bedroom. The camp bed came from his mother, who hates me because she's in her late sixties and doesn't think I'll get pregnant before she's snuffed it; she's probably right. It was Sean's idea to get the water bed for us, back when I was smaller, he thought it seemed romantic and exciting. I never told him that the sound of the water slapping against the mattress just made me want to go for a wee and that whenever we had sex I felt sea sick. Now that I'm larger I have to stay in one position all night; completely rigid, otherwise it sounds like a wave crashing against rocks during a storm if I try to roll over. That's why I don't dream often, it's hard to dream when you don't sleep.

But when I do dream I always dream of food; rich, fattening food, that I can feel stretching my skin as I swallow. Sometimes I dream that I am Willy Wonka in charge of my very own chocolate factory, but I am not the Wonka that Roald Dahl wrote about. I don't open my factory to eager little children clutching golden tickets; instead I swim in the chocolate river, not caring about polluting it. I pick candy flowers from the chocolate bushes and find gummy worms in the liquorice grass. I eat so much that the Oompa Loompa's have to build a bigger factory to contain me. It is always at this point in my dream that I wake up suddenly and the shame hits me like a punch in the face. I see my lovely, loyal husband lying fast asleep on his little camp bed in the corner and I know that he is dreaming of the life that we will have together, with our child, our fresh start. I know that he didn't sign up for this; I am not the woman he married.

"Sean," I whisper, "Are you awake?"

"No," he replies, his eyes still closed. His eyes have a little layer of sleep glue cementing his lashes onto his lids; it reminds me of when I used to wear fake eyelashes, struggling each morning on the train with the tiny tube of glue that always ended up smeared across my whole eyelid.

"It's nearly eight," I mumble, rolling myself onto my stomach and fumbling underneath my pillow, stopping only when I feel something cold beneath my fingers.

"What?" Sean leaps up, trying to open his eyes, rubbing them vigorously he attempts to shift some of the sleep and stares at me.

"Sarah you should've woken me, I'll be late. What are you doing?"

"I'm doing one of my morning exercises, Penny says it's a good way for me to get the blood circulating better in my legs," I lie, stretching my limbs out as far as they will go. I can feel the sweat beads forming on my forehead and my fringe sticking.

"Oh, right. Sounds like a good idea to me." he pauses, looking at me, "She's a good friend to you, is she popping in today?"

"Possibly, but she has WI on Wednesdays." As he turns to the wardrobe I roll my eyes, does he really think that Penny is my friend? Penny is the local busybody who comes round to stare at me like I'm a zoo attraction. I've heard her through the window; gossiping about me with my neighbours, telling them about poor unfortunate Sarah Button and her addiction to saturated fats, but she's part of the problem. She likes feeding me; she'll come round with huge Tupperware boxes filled with lasagne or family sized bags of crisps that will be left on my kitchen table, while I watch from the sofa with eyes as round as saucers. Penny always explains that the foods she brings is for Sean, "as you obviously can't go to the supermarket with your condition Sarah" she says this with a pitying look on her face that she must keep especially for funerals, or visits to the old people's home. It's the kind of look that says, "I'm here for you," when really she is secretly praying that I get bigger and bigger until I burst and she can tell the local paper that she tried to put me on the right track, whilst crying into an abundance of Kleenex.

"I have a meeting after work tonight," Sean says hesitantly, lining up shirts on the back of the wardrobe door. "The navy or the light blue?"

"Does it matter, they're both blue?" I say exasperatedly, as the cold bar beneath my fingers begins to feel warm.

"I'll go with the navy then," he replies, squirting a blob of clear gel into his hand and running it through his hair. It looks awful, like a hedgehog after a collision with a double decker bus. Spraying himself with aftershave he stands back to admire the finished result, "Are you coming down with me?"

"In a minute." I wait for him to leave then pull the chocolate bar out from under my pillow and inhale; it's almost melted in the time it has taken him to get dressed. He used to be so quick in the mornings, he'd be up and downstairs and then gone in a mad rush. Now he seems to spend forever preening and inspecting himself; he only works in insurance.

By the time I make it downstairs Sean is outside getting into his car. He waves to me at the window and I see him checking his mobile before he drives away. I wait for a message on my phone, but nothing appears. I stagger into the kitchen and see that Sean has left me a selection of food for the day. The sideboard is adorned with brightly coloured fruit; oranges, strawberries, bananas, blueberries and a huge pineapple. There is a tiny pot of hummus with some neatly cut carrot sticks in the fridge for my lunch and a bottle filled with a thick green liquid that is ominously labelled 'Green is Good J'. I ignore what Sean has given me, as always, and head for my boxes of cereal standing in pride of place next to the kettle. Sean never thinks to look at them because they are right in front of him, that's how I get away with it. He would never think I would be so bold as to hide food in the middle of the kitchen in plain sight. I open one of the boxes of muesli and empty it onto the kitchen table. Snickers, Crunchies, Milky Bars, dozens of packets of sweets and an assortment of toffees spill across the pine surface staring up at me like old friends. This is when I always feel at my worst; right before I devour each and every bar on the table. The hardest part of my deceit is seeing Sean so proud of me; he thinks I've lost two stone in weight, but actually I've put on just over three. I have to wear more black clothing now and hide myself under baggy tops and tracksuit bottoms. I have learnt that everything can be hidden in a tracksuit; especially stomach rolls and miniature Mars bars.

At 7pm Sean comes home, he looks uncomfortable. I notice him checking himself in the mirror before coming towards me, he smiles when he sees the empty smoothie bottle in the washing up bowl and only two pieces of fruit left.

"I'm sorry I'm back so late," he says softly, kissing me on my forehead. He smells different; of sweat and nerves. I just nod back at him, my mouth stuck together with a lump of toffee that I had already started eating before I heard his car in the driveway.

"You're doing so well Sarah, we'll get there. I promise you." Sean goes a little pink, like a child being caught doing something they shouldn't, and bows his head. Without another word he heads for the stairs and I can hear the bath running, he must be tired after the meeting. I quickly finish my toffee and empty my pockets of wrappers into the bottom drawer of my desk by the window. I pull back the curtains, it's starting to get dark outside but I can still make out the outline of the green compost bin; standing proudly by the garden fence, full of the fruit that was meant for me.

Hassan Hussein

Hassan is a third year English student who should be on the Drama route-way. He likes to add philosophical theories to everything – mostly contemporary plays. Occasionally, he writes scripts and was selected for Birmingham School of Acting's showreel. He likes his tea milky with one sugar.

The Look

EXT. BULL RING - DAY

FADE FROM BLACK:

Early morning rush hour - NANCY (37, simple,
structured, unsatisfied) clutches her shopping list
as she strides towards the entrance.

INT. BULL RING - DAY

DIEGO (19, passionate optimist) taps on the
escalator's rail

- wandering.

Scans around - something catches his eye.

Somebody.

Nancy.

He smirks to himself - walks away.

EXT. CROSSING - DAY

Nancy waits amongst a crowd of shoppers for the
flashing green sign - bags in one hand - shopping
list in another.

Green light flashes - she crosses - eyes on the
pavement in front.

She looks up.

Beat.

Her eyes are drawn to him - crossing from the
opposite side

- Diego.

He slows down - people brisk past him.

She slows down - people overtake her - a smile breaks through as she playfully directs her hair behind her ear.

A suited MAN jolts across the road, knocking her bags out of her hands.

She goes down to pick her things up - flustered.

Diego helps.

                    NANCY
          Thank you.

He stares into her eyes.

                    DIEGO
          No problem.

Beat.

Car beeps - they're in the way.

They quickly cross to their opposite sides. He looks back. So does she.

She laughs to herself as she runs her hands through her wavy hair - goes to walk away.

                    DIEGO
              (from across the road)
          Hey.

Nancy spins round.

                    DIEGO
          You dropped this.

He shakes her list in the air - she smiles.

EXT. CAFE - DAY

Large window of a quirky cafe - shoppers passing by.

Nancy and Diego sitting opposite one another -
lost in

conversation - bags at their feet - an
unintentional date.

INT. CAFE - DAY

Nancy studies Diego - tracing circles around
the rim of her coffee mug - placed on top of the
shopping list.

>   DIEGO
>   Was this on your list?

>   NANCY
>   I didn't think I'd get the chance to
>   grab something to eat.

>   DIEGO
>   And...

>   NANCY
>   And what?

A smile creeps through the corner of her mouth.

>   NANCY
>   And I didn't expect to speak to a
>   stranger.

>   DIEGO
>   (staring into his empty cup)

>   It's not really something I often do
>   either.

Diego looks at Nancy.

>   DIEGO
>   But I'm glad you dropped your list.

>   NANCY
>   I'm glad you found it.

EXT. CENTENARY SQUARE - NIGHT

Diego and Nancy walk down a dimly lit street -
slightly apart - the hustle and bustle of Broad
Street fades behind them.

A group of drunken students in the distance - He
clutches her closer to him - stampede averted.

She looks up to him - rests her head on his
shoulder. He grips her tighter.

She feels safe in his arms.

INT. BULL RING CAR PARK - NIGHT

Diego throws all of Nancy's shopping into the
boot.

She watches from behind, ruffles her hair with her
hands.

> DIEGO
>> All done.

He closes the boot.

> NANCY
>> My knight in shining armour.

He slides over to her - imitating a knight.

> NANCY
>> (Giggling)
>
> You're such an idiot.

Beat.

> DIEGO
>> You love it.

> NANCY
>> I need to go, I can't believe I've been
>> in town all day.

                    DIEGO
          What can I say.

He bows.

She glares at Diego - goes past him to get into
her car. She stops.

                    NANCY
          Thanks…for today.

                    DIEGO
          My pleasure.

He goes to walk away.

Beat.

                    NANCY
          You want a lift?

He turns around.

                    DIEGO
          I don't get into cars with strangers.

He winks and walks away.

Nancy gets into her car - takes a deep breath
- looks into her rear-view mirror - catches a
glimpse of Diego walking away.

She shakes her head.

Beat.

She gets out of the car - he turns around.

Nancy's walk slowly turns into a run - a run into
Diego arms.

                    NANCY
               (Muffled in Diego's chest)

          I... I

He holds her tightly - detaches her from his chest
- studying her face - her lips - eyes fixated.

Her eyes yearn for him - she surrenders.

Diego delicately places his hand on her cheek
- brushing her lips with his thumb - he smiles,
pulling her close.

They kiss.

INT. DINING ROOM - DAY

Nancy sitting on an oak dining table - littered
with paperwork, two breakfast plates - one empty,
one half eaten.

A phone goes off - she searches for it amongst the
sea of paper work.

She finds it - not the phone - the list.

> CHRISTIAN (O.S)
> Is my phone in there?

CHRISTIAN (40, smuggishly handsome) bursts into
the room, searching for his phone.

He notices Nancy immersed in the list - frozen.

> CHRISTIAN
> You get everything on the list, Nance?

She's fixated on the list.

> CHRISTIAN
> Nanc--

> NANCY
> --Yeah...yeah..sorry.

She puts the list down and locates Christian's
phone.

> CHRISTIAN
> What would I do without my gorgeous wife?

He kisses her on her head - takes phone.

> CHRISTIAN
> I'm off now - I don't know what time I'll
> be back so don't wait up.

                    Bye.

He leaves swiftly - door slams.

                         NANCY
                    Bye.

INT. CAR - NIGHT

Nancy parked outside her house - staring out
- thinking.

Christian leaves the house on his phone - he
notices her in the car.

                         NANCY
               I was just about to come in.

                         CHRISTIAN
               I've got to go back into the office.
               Don't wait up. Bye.

Christian walks off - Nancy left, deflated.

                         NANCY
                    Bye.

Nancy's text tone goes off - she jumps.

She picks her phone up - reads her message
- smiles.

EXT. APARTMENT BLOCK - NIGHT

Nancy presses number 13's buzzer - impatiently
waits - constantly fixing her hair - shivering in
the cold.

Buzzed in.

INT. APARTMENT CORRIDOR - NIGHT

Nancy knocks number 13.

                    DIEGO (O.S)
          Who is it?

                    NANCY
          Who do you think?

                    DIEGO
          I don't know, my mother told me not to
          speak to strangers.

                    NANCY
          Let me in!

He opens the door - wide grin plastered on his
face.

                    DIEGO
          Welcome to my humble abode.

He takes her hand - kisses it - leads her inside.

INT. DIEGO'S LIVING ROOM - NIGHT

Diego quickly decorates his living room with an
array of scented candles - art pieces hang on the
walls - warm and inviting.

A bottle of prosecco and two glasses sit on his
small table. He forgets the strawberries - goes
out - brings them in - admiring his efforts.

Beat.

                    DIEGO
          Hurry up, Nancy - you've been in the
          bathroom for ages!

He lights all the candles - dims the lights.

                    NANCY (O.S)
          I'm coming--

INT. DIEGO'S BATHROOM - NIGHT

Nancy sits on the edge of the bath - she stares at

herself in the mirror opposite.

She takes out her phone from her pocket - she rings her husband - it rings out.

She tries again - his phone is now off - she's left with his answering machine.

>   CHRISTIAN (V.O)
>   You've reached Christian Drew, I'm either
>   busy or ignoring you, please leave a
>   message after the beep.

She cuts off - fixes herself in the mirror.

INT. DIEGO'S LIVING ROOM - NIGHT

Nancy walks in - she stops - tears fill her eyes - she's not used to this.

>   NANCY
>   D… Diego, you shouldn't have.

He goes over to her and delicately wipes her tear away.

>   DIEGO
>   Saves electricity.

>   NANCY
>   Idiot.

She notices the artwork hung on the walls - intrigued.

>   NANCY
>   Is that your work?

>   DIEGO
>   (scratching his neck)

>   Yeah...

He grabs her closer - they kiss - his mouth moves towards her neck - she succumbs to her desires.

Beat.

She pushes him off - goes over to the prosseco - drinks it from the bottle.

Diego stands back - admires her, his finger tracing his lips.

EXT. BEDROOM - NIGHT

Large window of Diego's dimly lit bedroom.

He carries Nancy into his bedroom - her legs wrapped around his stomach - locked in an embrace - kissing his neck.

Diego falls back onto his bed - Nancy on top - taking off his t-shirt — lip-locked.

He flips her over - He's on top - takes off her blouse. They continue to toss and turn - removing an item of clothing piece by piece - exploring each others' bodies.

Sexual - passionate - sensual - energetic.

INT. BEDROOM - DAY

Nancy wakes up - scans the room, confused - turns around to see Diego peacefully asleep - smiles to herself - snuggles up to him.

INT. CAFE - DAY

Same quirky cafe from their first date - breakfast for two.

> DIEGO
> So when is it my turn to be wined and dined?

Beat.

Nancy looks down.

                    DIEGO
          I understand...

                    NANCY
          Understand what?

                    DIEGO
          That I set the bar quite high.

Nancy throws a mushroom at Diego.

                    DIEGO
          Hey!

He leans over and kisses her. Nancy smiles.

Beat.

                    NANCY
          I love you.

EXT. UNIVERSITY CAMPUS - DAY

Diego searches for his building - campus map in
one hand - backpack in the other.

First day of university - art undergraduate.

EXT. SCHOOL OF ART - DAY

Diego bounces up the steps.

INT. SCHOOL OF ART - DAY

Diego checks his timetable - Contemporary and
Historical Contexts - room 13, level 3 - 10am.

                    DIEGO
               (checks his phone)

          Shit, I'm late.

Diego runs over to the lifts - out of order - he
goes for the stairs.

INT. SCHOOL OF ART, LEVEL 3 - DAY

Diego stands in the middle of the corridor - looks
to the left - looks to the right.

                    DIEGO
          Room 6, room 8...

He walks up a bit.

                    DIEGO
          Room 13.

He peers through the windowpane of the classroom
door.

Beat.

He stops - Something catches his eye.

Someone.

Nancy - his teacher.

FADE TO BLACK.

Rochelle McKiernan

Rochelle was born in Solihull in 1987. She is currently doing her MA in Writing. She can mainly be found in her bedroom; reading, writing or dancing. She enjoys exploring and Jarvis Cocker.

You can take your Year in Provence and shove it up your arse.

Girls

This is for the girls
Who lay there
Close
With their own personal Adonis or, Venus
Lust engulfing your limbs, love flooding your brain
You make love, again
Then, he coolly walks away.
Fucked.

Black Boots

My little black boots
Sitting in the hallway-

And heart, barely beating
In his hands

Wildflower

A white bud shivers,
Flowering beauty soars,
This death as light snow falls.

Bed

This young heart whispers
Forbidden love stirs,
This time after the storm.

Rhoda Greaves

Rhoda Greaves is a PhD Creative Writing student at Birmingham City University. Her writing credits include being highly commended in the Manchester Fiction Prize, and shortlisted in the Bridport and Aesthetica Short Story Prizes. Her short stories have been accepted for publication in several literary magazines including Short Fiction Journal, Cake, The View From Here, and Litro. *The Blue Room* has been previously published in Stories with Pictures and FlashFlood Journal.

The Blue Room

We painted the walls together. Alex had already picked the colour. Had some hippy notion we should blend in seamlessly with our surroundings; be at one with the sky. A whole year we spent in this place, our skin turning salty; lickable. Just the two of us photographing seabirds, ticking off lists.

"You'll get bored, Cass," Mum had warned me. But Alex and I answered the advert anyway. His degree in biological science and my experience at the sanctuary easily secured us the gig.

We couldn't wait to set up the telescopes that first evening, almost as soon as the helicopter touched us down. Made ourselves potted meat sandwiches with apples and coffee. Celebrated the summer ahead of us, as we listened to the birds tucking up their young ones, hiding our eyes from the strawberry-coated sun. We'd never have believed that when the rain did come, it would pound so hard we'd think the ceiling might cave in.

You were born right there on that battered old armchair. If you'd waited just a little longer, we'd have been safely back on the mainland, readying a makeshift nursery in the spare bedroom at Mum's.

Alex rang three nines, of course, but the tide was as playful as a bullmastiff puppy: a bunch of holidaying kids had strayed out too far with their nets and buckets – got caught on the rocks, and had to scream and wave for help. While their parents anxiously watched the rescue, I crossed my legs and pressed my face to the mothballed fabric. Prayed you'd hang on till somebody came.

Like just-wound clockwork, Alex paced from window to

window to window, scanning the empty horizon for dots. It was him who noticed first; a dark trickle staining the soft beige upholstery. I was too busy sinking my teeth into it. Calling out for Mum, and timing gaps.

"Cass," he said. "Oh God, Cass, you're bleeding." He pulled at my knickers, just as you crowned.

You were quick for a firstborn, slippery, uncatchable. Neither of us knew to feel for the cord.

It seemed like the right time to come back here; to do this. How could I not notice the rising damp, or the peeling paintwork, the trailing cables? Or the smashed in windows lining each wall? Your chair's where it always was, but the seat has gone missing. No one can tell you've long been scrubbed away.

I make for the window, the blue of the sky beyond it, as broken glass crunches under foot like shimmery pink shells. My fingers fumble at the clasp of the heart-shaped locket I've worn at my neck for eighteen years now. I take in the blurry coastline, hear the lone call of a cormorant. And I blow your ashes on the wind.

Michael Hawthorn

Michael is a second-year English Student. His prevailing characteristic is laziness. He like little things and is regarded by friends as scruff. In his adult life he has studied, travelled, studied, and will travel again once his studying is done. He writes because he can't do other stuff.

December 2014

I stepped into the streets of Birmingham with nowhere to go. For two nights I was going to be homeless. My first thought was to find shelter from the wind, which, sweeping along the December frost, had already begun taking its toll. I remembered how as a boy, coming back from football on the M6 in my dad's car, I'd wind down the windows from the back seat so the wind could thunder in and buffet me about. I'd close my eyes and imagine battling blizzards, scaling mountains, sailing on tempestuous seas, then quickly roll them back up to enjoy the suffusing warmth. This night the wind gave me no such taste for adventure. I saw it stripping trees of leaves. I saw it dragging crisp packets and bags. I felt it biting relentlessly, and had no handle to shut it out.

It was the early hours of the morning when I set off. The streets were silent, empty. I started walking aimlessly through the Jewellery Quarter, looking for nooks to crawl into. I even paused at a few doorways darkened with piss, but the thought of it was worse even than the smell of it. Eventually, I just sat under a bridge. I tried to collect any thoughts but I was too numb and they were too slippery. I wanted to set up some plan for the night, so that I wouldn't freeze by morning, or get caught in a sudden downpour of rain, but couldn't concentrate. There was nothing to be done. It was too cold for thought.

Once I'd left the bridge, I found a hostel called Waterside House and tried, with all the pathos I could muster, to get a room. From where I stood in the doorway, pretending to read whatever they had posted up there – running through my head what I should say so they would let me in, I could see two men eyeing me from behind a counter. They had pens and forms and stern faces. To their left was a door with glass panes damming dark behind it; a door beyond which, I figured, were stairs to rooms where the homeless lay asleep. I told them that due to unforeseeable circumstances I had found myself sleeping on the streets, and required a place to stay. They told me there was no room, that you had to check in early to have any chance, and then, after some rushed directions to the Salvation Army, they sent me on my way. I tried to follow their instructions but got lost among office blocks. It was nearing dawn when I finally claimed my bed: a gap between a billboard and a wall. I climbed in and slept.

Having no appetite for dreams, I closed the space between waking and sleep in an instant, so that morning scolded me just as soon as I shut my eyes. My nest was sprayed with frost. I shot up, fumbled for a foothold on the wall to boost myself up, shuffled sideways along the top – the hands feeling their way along the back of the billboard for support, branches braking off my back to remake my bed below – and jumped into the street. It was as grey as ever. I started running down the road, desperate to warm up. Bits of twig and leaf shivered off me as I went. I headed for the city centre, intending to spend the morning loitering in shops – occasionally picking up products at random to uphold a veneer of patronage. Not knowing my home town as well as I should, however, I hit Chamberlain Square before any store could lure me in, and decided I'd be better off at the library, where I could sit and sleep while pretending to read. I ran right up to the entrance and let the escalators do the rest. Once alone, I dropped into a modern wing-back by a window and swiped the nearest book to hand: *Napoleon's Fatal March on Moscow*. I braced myself for the unassailable Russian winter. I immediately fell asleep.

I woke at twilight with the preface pressed to my chest. The library had emptied. From the window I could see the German market sharpening its glow with nightfall. I could see small cabins and beechen stalls all light-laced and spilling steam into the air. I could hear, faintly, festive songs that no matter how cynical I grow with age simply cannot shed their charm. I saw the blissful young drinking from tankards, and figures swerving on the ice rink away to my right in blurred orbits of varying speeds. It was the picture of Christmas. I returned *Napoleon's March on Moscow* roughly in its place and returned to the street.

The sight of rough sleepers soon rid me of my Christmas spirit. The virus had not spread to them. They didn't dawdle at hatches for the tat, nor queue for frankfurters. They were despondent, silent, apart. They went so unnoticed, they seemed part of the architecture of the city, like gargoyles perched at the edges of buildings, watching. I wondered what they thought of while the world wended by in lines – their bags bursting with obligatory gifts, their cheeks bulging with treats. What memories did they cling to? To one man I saw (a heap of hair and clothes) the crowd didn't exist at all, or seemed not to. He was sat upright and staring; reposed in the sunset as though before him swept ocean and not men. I wanted to know what went wrong, to know how steep the slopes were, to talk to him, to help. But before anything could come to mind I was washed away with the rest of them shuffling together in anonymous forever-onward currents.

I lost sight of the homeless once the market closed and everyone piled into taxis. I supposed they retired to whatever homes they had. As I turned off the market, onto a side-road leading to the station, a pretty girl pulled her head out of a nearby black-cab window to yell at relatives, 'over here! He said it'll be about forty quid,' and for the first time, I felt compelled to go home. The girl's family came over to the cab with such homely togetherness, I wanted them to take me in. They looked like they were going to sit beside a log fire, where granddad pours brandy into everyone's glass (even a smidgen for the kids who with one sniff wince), and the fir throbs purple and blue, humming languor throughout the house. If she'd asked me along, and all their chubby grins then turned on me in welcome, I'd have given it all up. I wanted to be saved.

Once the thought of them had passed, I was ashamed; I pitied myself more than I pitied the real homeless. This made me feel despicable.

After a couple more hours of wandering, I sat on a bench outside WHSmith's awhile, hoping to recharge. I closed my eyes and slumped forward like an expired cyborg. I was like a segment of the city already. Young lovers passed at a frequent rate, laughing as they went by – not towards me (they were too cocooned in it all to notice me) but generously, towards everything. It was that constant flux of joy, as though the pituitary gland had ruptured and was overloading the body, causing it to feed out over the edges and into the world without particular excitement. One girl shouted at me to 'wake up!' but I didn't mind. I mustn't have looked very homeless; only downtrodden and a bit lost. I continued wandering.

I walked for nine hours on that final night, stopping only occasionally to rest my back. I tried to sleep in a bush, but the cold made it impossible. An overgrown patch of land between Aston University Campus and the canal seemed the best bet for some sleep, for there were these open containers in the tall grass where discarded office equipment was being stored. The design of these containers caused them to bend back on themselves, making a sort of S-shaped shelter from the wind. In one, I found sodden carpet tiles that I piled up for a bed and a large board with a thin layer of spongy skin to lay over me. In this first container, however, the walls were lifted slightly from the turf, so that the wind crept in from beneath, whistling through pinched metal and getting through gaps in my clothes to my skin. It was useless.

The second container I saw was covered with shrubs, which made it look tucked-up tight. But inside, two larva-like figures murmured and rustled their sleeping-bags when I came too close. Taking this for discontent, I spun round and left just as quickly as I went in. As cold as I was, it did not seem right that a person less than a day away from home should impinge on the comfort of those who slept out there nightly. Knowing this would've brought me no comfort at all.

After failing to find suitable digs, I decided I'd walk till sunrise. The sign at the bus stop told me I had four hours before the first bus home, so I picked a path towards Broad St. to see what lunacy alcohol had freed. I regretted the decision as soon as I got there. Night clubs spewed noise and nonsense into the street; men bellowed; women shrieked; clowns on stilts rained down leaflets, shouting discounts at passers-by; angry young men scowled, and prowled for weaker young men to fight with; gorgeous girls skidded dead-eyed from chip-shop doorways, being pursued by prancing goons – their chips dripped onto the pavement and were squished, so that the fluff was spat out from within, looking new-born, until another sloppy footstep smeared it flat: half to concrete, half stuck up in the shoe. Stupidity abounded. It was the very principle of the street. I had never been alone there before, never sober. It was no place to stand abstracted. I hurried, head down, past all of it, right to the end of the road where only loneliness and ennui could greet me. Dawn was all I wanted now.

I spent the rest of the night in McDonald's, waiting for the first bus home. I'd lost sight of what I set out to do. I thought living on the street would freshen my perspective, or put me in touch with a group of people commonly screened, yet all I wanted was my bed. I felt no nearer to the homeless at all. The truth is, spending two nights on the street is nothing like having to live there. I knew from the beginning I'd soon be out of the cold, and that I only had to endure until then. Those that deal with the cold, the hunger, the loneliness, the lack of power every day, have the despair of it all to deal with also. Their suffering has no certain end. They were outside, getting whatever sleep they could, while I sat in McDonald's listening to teenagers discussing relationship problems. I heard one girl repeat, "It's me. *I'm* being stupid. *I'm* being weird. But I don't like it when James has got his hands on Clare's waist," over and over again to her friends on a nearby table. They looked 15 years old and spoke like they were in the throes of divorce.

James was sat at another table, telling a fringe with legs how it was all just harmless fun. He can't help himself, you see. He was an impressive twat. He had it pegged, he really did. He managed to sound like a victim and a hero in the same breath. I couldn't guess what function was on in town – perhaps I'd inadvertently stumbled into a live recording of *The Only Way is Birmingham*, it's hard to tell – but these kids were everywhere, and making a tremendous mess. Every table other than mine was infested with rubbish. The floor at their feet had burger wrappings, plastic straws, ketchup sachets strewn. It looked like a post-apocalyptic waste ground. Only, instead of the bedraggled scavengers sifting through the scraps, there were these gleaming Topshop mannequins callously stocking the piles. It was far too easy to loathe them.

I watched the night's stragglers come and go until at last I saw the sun. A Christian preacher who screams, "come to Jesus!" near the old ramp to New St. Station, came into McDonald's right before my bus was due and started singing over Paul McCartney's, *Simply Having a Wonderful Christmas Time*. Rather than singing the words McCartney intended, however, he sang, loud enough so that the original version was quite drowned out, "simply having a wonderful Jesus time! Simply having a wonderful *loving-god* time! Simply having..." on and on, even after the song itself had stopped. I think he was preaching the true meaning of Christmas. I almost choked on my drink when he continued singing it on his way out the door. I watched him jig off towards the ramp, right until he slipped the bend. Then I went home.

Maria Lourens

Maria is currently possessed by: A.S. Byatt, the art history of Coventry (yes, there is such a thing!), Philip Larkin, George Eliot and all things ISIS. Maria made her way from South Africa, through North Africa, Algeria, Morocco to the UK and currently teaches and lives in Shenzhen, China.

Poetry 2

Oh you killed it in the traditional Muslim way -
you took great care to conceal the deceit
when you packed the backpack with all that is explosive:
the five pillars and the innocence of children.
You carefully cloaked your naked erection
With piety and Islamia:
You strapped it onto my unsuspecting heart
And with Allahu Akhbar!
You blew it all apart

Poetry 5

When they snipped the foreskin off your penis
you stretched it over the darbuka
and started banging the drum
for all that is halal and haram

And now your problem is the penis
seeking skin from Algerie to gay Paris
drugs and alcohol so forbidden
but it is sex that leaves you quite bedridden

Poetry 7

The prayer call rips right through my heart
and leaves the shattered shards
on the bouldered beach at La Madrague

I light a candle at Madame Afrique
for all that braved the shores before
but I know in my heart's core:
It is only Camus I am looking for

I can cover my head in a veil
and wrap my body in black,
wear a crown and carry a cross on my back
or prostrate on a prayer mat

But I place the hope in a carefully chosen casket
and sink it deep into the earth
I play a requiem for all your beliefs
and know, in stanza soliloquy and mirth
I will celebrate my rebirth

China Poetry 5

Should I hold you accountable
for a square stained with blood
Should I remind you
of Monks without rights
or recall lives without votes

Should I speak of people purposely starved, or
of little girls drowned in chamber pots
or quietly suffocated in hostile cots

For where I come from
my country bears the blot
of history filled with hate
Actually that's why I am here:
My China life without care nor fear

China Poetry 6

A much needed Noah's Ark
built on the Shaanxi Road
when Cherry trees blossomed
you fixed the mezuzah to the door
fitted your yarmulke snugly
and lit the brass menorah

Then Netanyao suddenly forgot
the words of Zachariah:
Not by might, not by power,
but by My Spirit

Now the Hamesh Hand
 watches over your land
as you shut the door
and turn Arab land
to rubble and sand

Leanne Falconer

Leanne is a 22 year old English and Drama BA student. A self-professed dilettante, she spends her time getting distracted by online shopping when she should be working, as well as biding her time until creative ideas are able to write themselves down. She recently wrote a play and can't stop going on about it.

Dora

I always wondered what kind of life Billy's cat had had before she was adopted. His family didn't seem to know anything about her, except that she'd been found cowering in a blanket behind some old bin bags.

She was a small calico named Dora; she had green eyes much too large for her face. I gravitated toward her. There was never a time when I didn't feel the need to be holding or stroking her. The first time I met Billy's parents, Dora padded around me several times before Billy's dad had to drag her away.

This didn't stop her from finding her way over to me once Billy's mom had, reluctantly, offered me a seat on the sofa. While Dora purred her way into my heart, Billy's parents cleared their throats more than necessary all the while asking questions and making small talk.

I would have been counting the minutes until Billy and I went up to his room had it not been for how comfortable Dora made me.

As we made our way up the stairs, Billy's dad called after us.

"Leave the door open, will you, boys," he said.

Billy made a point of sighing. He didn't comply.

Billy always made a point of sighing if he didn't like or agree with something. After a while it really started to get on my nerves. If something made him unhappy, he needed everyone to know about it. He certainly didn't get that trait from his parents who were pros at smiling and feigning ease in the face of all things.

It wasn't long before Dora began following me upstairs to Billy's room whenever I would visit. Billy would be recounting the details of football practice and I'd become distracted by her scratching at the door and poking her paws through the gap at the bottom. He sighed and let her in, if only so that I would regain my focus.

This approach didn't always work. If Billy was trying to initiate something romantic, Dora was a bother whether she was in or out of the room. The scratching, the paws. This became a sore spot for us.

One evening, Billy suggested watching a film. I could already hear Dora playing around in the hallway.

"What should we watch?" He asked.

"Anything, I'm not fussed."

"You always say that, and then you moan at whatever I pick."

"That's because you always pick the director's cut of something that was already bollocks in the first place," I said.

"You never pay attention anyway."

"Because it's boring."

"Because you're always preoccupied with the bloody cat," he shouted.

There was a moment of silence then. Billy had never shouted at me before, not even as a joke. I shouted at him all the time, it was in my nature.

Billy sighed. I sighed.

"Who taught you that word?" I asked him.

"What?"

"'Preoccupied.' You didn't learn that playing footie with the lads," I said.

He sighed. He laughed. Dora scratched at the door. He let her in.

Even though she was tall enough and smart enough, Dora was always polite enough to scratch at the door until it was opened for her, rather than letting herself in. That was, however, as far as her manners extended.

Every time Billy and I began watching whichever dreadful

film he had picked out for us, Dora would pounce onto my lap just as the movie reached what Billy called 'the good bit'. These movies were long and tiresome and required much more concentration that I was willing to give and Dora ruined every single one.

Whenever Billy and I began to kiss, Dora would pounce on top of us just as we reached what I called 'the good bit'. These kisses were long and adoring and required just as little concentration as I was willing to give and Dora ruined every single one.

Eventually Billy said we had to start going my house, which was never a problem to begin with but he was intent on rubbing our relationship in his own parents' faces and forcing them to deal with it, to get over it.

But I missed Dora.

There was something almost dull in knowing no one was going to interfere when Billy and I kissed. There was nothing stopping us from kissing for hours which I suppose was better than the dreadful never-ending bore-fests that were Billy's favourite films.

I suppose I could have picked a different film but it would be hard to watch with Billy sighing beside me the whole way through.

I missed Dora and so, much to his parents' dismay, I convinced Billy to start taking me back to his.

"Oh, Jake!" his mother said when I walked into the lounge for the first time in weeks.

"Nice to see you," his father said, but I could tell it wasn't really.

It showed in the way we exchanged polite, tight and unwilling smiles with each other. Nothing like the smiles I gave when Dora appeared. She came straight over to me and I didn't hesitate to scoop her up and take her straight upstairs with me.

"You and that bloody cat," Billy said.

"You and your bloody complaining," I sniped.

The remainder of our relationship consisted of me with Dora

and Billy with his complaints. He always accused me of loving her more than I loved him.

"You're blaming a cat for problems in our relationship," I said.

"She is the problem."

"You think if you got rid of Dora everything would be fine?"

"Obviously, Jake."

"Oh, you idiot! Even if you got rid of Dora, you'd still be a whiny little prick!" I shouted.

"Right, then you can fuck off. Get out. You won't be seeing me or the cat again," he said, picking up Dora in one hand and using the other to nudge me towards the door.

"You ought to be a little bit nicer to her," I said. "In the end she's going to be all you have left."

In hindsight, it was a little harsher than it needed to be but I didn't regret it. The truth was I'd always miss her more than I missed him.

Guy Etchells

Guy has a creativity and optimism that is boundless. Quickly establishing himself as a writer who can succeed in multiple genres.

A Hedge Full of Sparrows

Two children, a husband, a small two-up-two down house and a garden filled with convolvulous, lilliums, agapanthus, white Japanese anemones, scented jasmine and clematis. When she was a young woman this was all Margaret had dreamed of. They all seemed such minor things to crave, but it had been all she truly wanted. Now the children were all grown up, creating their own lives finding their own desires. Her husband, William, had passed away three years ago, but for Margaret the last thing she felt was sad. She knew more than anyone that she had been blessed. Her thoughts told her it was a time to celebrate life and all the events that had brought her to this place and this way of feeling right now. Was she not extremely lucky, privileged and honoured to have raised two children? To have shared her life with a man she has loved so effortlessly until death did they part?

It had not always been like this. She had been the weary mother, the emotional wife, and the underpaid, under-appreciated employee, and she, like so many others had lost sight of the things around that are taken for granted, while fighting the seemingly endless battle that was life.

Margaret believed she had been given a unique gift, the gift to gain happiness and appreciation in the simplest things. It wasn't the fancy cars, large house, designer clothes and endless attempts to accumulate more money, believing millions will bring prolonged happiness. She believed she was richer than that in so many ways. The things that made her life a joy from day to day, week to week, were to be found in the simplest of things, even in a hedge full of sparrows.

She sat on the sun bleached bench at the top of the garden next to the privet hedge, a mug of tea in her hand. It had become somewhat of a ritual these past years. From this vantage point Margaret could look down upon the rest of her garden. What amused her while sitting cradling her mug, was the never-ending goings on of the sparrows in the hedge. One moment the hedge would be empty, then without warning, a flock of sparrows would shoot through the garden and land in the privet, and what a noise they made. What was even more surprising was that most of the time she could barely see them, but they would make such a racket, twittering and chirping just like quarrelling children in a play ground. Were they arguing or fighting? Clearly they were excited, and throughout the summer they treated the hedge like a youth club, a place to meet and chat, but from an observer's perspective it sounded more like cheeky squabbling. It had kept Margaret transfixed to the point where she had lost all awareness of time. She would laugh out loud while attempting to understand what all the bickering was about. What could be going on in their little heads? Every so often one sparrow would appear as if to gather its strength before returning into the unseen chaos. It was better than any soap opera Margaret always thought. It was an endless source of amusement that would be repeated on a daily basis, weather permitting.

On cool summer evenings with a delicate blanket around her shoulder, Margaret watched the birds begin to roost for the evening. The wood pigeon with its gentle rhythmic tone would soon give way to the blackbird that as self proclaimed king of the garden would perch atop the highest conifer and give a final performance offering praise and thanks for the day. She would stare transfixed at an unending sky as it grew dim, the last rays of sunlight setting alight the distant clouds that moved like silk through an amber sky. These things, these parts of life are taken for granted; they don't cost much if anything at all and collectively, they assemble into a symphony of pleasures to be remembered always.

She smiled to herself at the thought of what had been another beautiful day and continued smiling, knowing that another would be born in a matter of hours and that she would be there to greet it.

Anthony Mellors

Anthony Mellors is Professor of Poetry and Poetics at Birmingham City University. Recent work includes *The Lewknor Turn* (Shearsman, 2013), and *The Christmas Album* (Verisimilitude, 2015). Soon there will be poems in the final issue of *Vlak*, and *Sylphs* (with Penny Hallas) will be a Five Seasons Press Broadside. The essay 'Modernism after Modernism' forms the final chapter of the forthcoming Cambridge *History of Modernist Poetry*.

for jeff hilson

What were these you have loved, jeff?
These you do love these you will have
loved these you would have loved had
you known about them these that might
have been loved had they but love to give
and had you been in the right place at the
right time the future past the anterior
interior the pre-amp phase 4 funkatronic
ultra fidelity lautsprecher mordaunt
short beovox disco galactic realistic
teak adoration in the right time right
last the whole night long kind of place
latin world kind of place solid gold
hammond moog party time y los trios strip
tease 101 strings play songs of old england
with that latin feel kind of place immortal
serenades wunderlich pops mexican
tijuana shane rimmer goes bossa quim
barreiros cracklin' rosie dream liebestraum
pop orgel hitparty sing and dance with caterina
valente memories are made of this tico
tico el bimbo kind of place time a
time and a place always on my mind
whistling in the wires take this job
and shove it little children everywhere
time esta muchacho various artists manuel
ecstasy time frank chacksfield
easy marimba party time call me

irresponsible as time goes by time where
do I begin nonstop double hammond there's
a kind of hush tweedle dee spanish eyes
trumpet a gogo happy lehar bittet zum
tanz folge time violins in love beachparty
excess of seventy million albums
rock-a-doodle I knew jesus all my friends
are dead time liberace plays dancing
skeletons by candlelight impossible
dreamtime without a worry in the world alone
after dark have a nice day with lena martell
hasta manana the look of love the touch
of your lips the touch of melachrino
in living stereo the touch of andre kostelanetz
the magnificent pianos of ronnie aldrich these
you love have loved will have loved place time

An ordinary evening in Newhaven

warps around the property
high levels of pickup on the shingle spit
joysticks control enormous grabbers
engage with incinerator flue gas
a convenient dumping-ground
crunch of gears on the hillside
stack top or downwind levels

we can leverage that value chain
dark and sentimental
once loved but not recalled

perforated bottoms
nozzles
clinker
dioxin cracking
fly ash
sludge

for Ian Marchant

Chuck Newsey

Chuck Newsey is an American writer working towards an MA degree in Writing and the 2014 holder of the Jim Crace Fiction Award . Chuck has lived more than nine lives; exceeding a feisty cat. Chuck has been the hero, the victim, the confidant, the liar, and was homeless for a time.

One day, Chuck hopes to race a tumbleweed.

Desertion

She woke up in the desert, and rubbed the sand out from her eyes.

The sun, Nevada in style but Arizonian in force, was unforgiving, brute, and obtuse. It had blinded her, momentarily—the vacant setting of a subtle beige gradient gradually came into view. First, a cactus; tall and solitary with prickled thorns kept everything at a distance. Then a single vulture soared in the distance, dark and mean yet graceful in flight; a wanderer.

She sat up with a groan and memorized the surrounding sand. It settled into a panoramic monotony. The desert, a platform of vacancy where population simmered to a whispered hush— understood only in past tense, as nothing in the desert survives. She heard a noise, the nearly undetectable sound of sifting sand, a quiet movement. She turned against the sun and looked behind her. A boy lay a few feet away, shielding his eyes.

"Easy now," he told her with a gentle voice. The words were received with a warbled tone, and as she began to wake toward a silhouette.

"Good morning." It was a near whisper, but hoarse.

"Morning."

"What happened last night?" She crawled closer to him, and messed the smooth sand.

"You came upon my desert town; filled with bitter men."

She did not, could not recall this.

"You told me you could save me, and I followed you."

That does not sound like me, she thought, but she did not, could not know for sure. There was a small wretchedness in this freedom. Even wrapped in the desert warmth she was cold from things unknown.

"You said when we heard the Mermaid's song then we've made it."

Now that sounds like me, but she did not, could not know for sure.

It was a Sunday, or so she thought, but it was actually a Tuesday. The sun, though young in the day, shined brilliantly, and reflected every granule of the desert sand. She seemed alone, and in a way she was. The boy sat with dried lips, crusty and white.

He was a stranger, and she resembled his closest friend from earlier days. A girl once known so well to him; so intimate and pure. She had green eyes and light hair that was permanently fixed into two long braids; so lovely and innocent. As children they were lovers; not of body, but of mind.

He watched the girl rub the remaining sand from her eyes. She was a perpetual stranger; without a memory— a wanderer soaring on land who had no choice but to wander. Perpetually. He saw her as the child she once was. His eyes grew soft and curious at the sight of those braids, the cheerful smile of moments past. The rough grains and lines of her aged body had not perverted his view of her. The adult maturation laid untouched, the youthful vision of supple skin and mind for curiosity.

Yesterday, on the eve of their desert morning, an incidental clamour of bells and chimes from the local church rang and echoed in a loud resonance. It welcomed her to the town filled with shanties; it pulsated within her. She appeared happy, and in a way she was. She knew of no troubles and the bright sun was pleasing to her skin. The gentle but apparent wind brushed her braided hair to and fro and swung back to forth, forth to back with each step in the desert town. She was nameless, like Holly Golightly's cat. She was a book half-read, bed half-made, hair half-uncombed.

A few miles away in a diner that bordered the desert line, the boy felt the small clangs of the church bell sounds in the distance. The sound seemed to unite them. The boy seemed to wallow the days away, cooped up in the shanty town affixed with a permanent grimace. It was a wild western fury of unbridled and perpetual thoroughfare. This shanty town should never be a destination, only a route.

Yesterday, the girl blew into the town like a tumbleweed, or so she thought. She found solace in a diner on the outskirts of the town. It was damp, brooding and unimpressive; the décor immense but without pretension, a forgettable place. She took a seat at the counter and slumped into a stupor that was without aid of drugs, but of a pure, menacing disintegration of mind. Of a wanderer who had seen too many sights, all discarded like the many dreams in sleep.

She was a wanderer who knew nothing. She did not, and could not care for anyone.

"Who are you?" the girl asked, and she shook her head. "I meant to ask what time it is."

Right then and there, he had no doubts. He studied her, watched her, the pierce of her green eyes and light hair rattled him; uncanny. He remembered the image of the girl he left alone, oh so long ago.

"It's roughly seven in the evening, darling," he paused. "But you do know me."

She did not, could not recall this. His face was serious. She searched hidden thoughts of things to remember.

"I left you in ruins."

She did not, could not recall him, but his words felt true. "Oh so long ago."

Though silent, their minds roared.

His, of an innocent love and tickle fights near the seaside in a place far away, a distant and forgotten life, abruptly cut short by the too painful memory of their parting; of a day too grim and sour to recover in full thought.

Hers, of a falsehood, lies, a life constructed from the implication of his words. In essence, she thought of nothing. But she was his kitten with an unknown Name, and she belonged to him.

"Hurts like home," he confided.

"Where is home?" she asked.

"Wherever I am not."

"I can save you."

She lead the boy out from the diner, the sleaze and grease heavy in the stale air slid off of them the further they wandered on. He held onto her hand and followed her obediently, for he seemed pleased to be headed in some direction. She seemed to have a destination in mind, and in a way she did. The large sun drew lower and lower, deeper and down, descending in grand proportion. She took forty-nine barefoot paces toward the Dalai Lama, the steps audible with the soft trampling of granular sediment beneath their feet. The girl had stopped suddenly and she fixed her eyes on a mirage that glistened in surreptitious wonderment hovering in the distance. The image was serene and furtive, the sound of a somber harmony, its echo captive in the shallow resonance of a boundary-less aquarium.

"We're here," the girl told the boy, and she collapsed in the darkening sand; the song cooed her into slumber. The day erased.

When morning came, she rubbed the sand out from her eyes with so many questions unasked, unanswered, unknown.

"What is the time?" the boy asked himself and looked toward the sun.

"It's early," she assessed.

"I have to work."

They got up and began the walk back to the shanty life, unstepping their steps from the previous night. They walked in silence, a hot balmy silence. He was not finished with her, he had so many things to ask, answer, know.

"I'll be finished early in the evening, if you want to talk."

Why? she thought.

"Find a room for the night, there's the B&B on Lily Lane." He pointed to the west to a despairing row of shanty dwellings, prettied with small clusters of white desert lilies. "They'll take care of you."

The girl nodded. "Meet me."

In silence they departed. He disappeared into the diner on the outskirt of the town. She disappeared to the west and stole a lily from a dry and vacant yard. She twirled it as she walked, the growing heat of the desert day made her sweat, the drops from her forehead created a dew that dripped onto the flower. She placed it in her light hair. The braids were knotted; unkempt, undone from a night of unrest in the desert. She had a childish disregard for appearance; she did not care for neatness, but felt pretty with delicate accessories.

She came upon a lodging house halfway down the lane. It was the tallest building in sight, three stories. A humble sign hung on the wooden door that read Lily Inn. A man sat behind the desk and chewed on a straw; the mangled plastic swished and gathered salivation in his tiny mouth. He looked at her and slowly removed the straw.

"Haven't seen yah inna while, Miss."

She wiped her brow with her hand, dirty from the desert sand.

"I met someone."

"Have you naw. Gee, 'bout time summon took yer fancy." The man placed the straw back in his mouth and took a key from a hook on the wall behind him.

"Have a gudd'n naw."

"Thanks." She looked at the key and saw 2B scribbled in faded black marker, and headed up the stairs.

In the evening, the boy left the diner, worn from a day's work, and passed clusters of lilies.

"Sshir." The man nodded with the straw still in his mouth. "2B."

"Sir." The boy nodded and walked up the stairs.

He knocked on the door and she welcomed him. Her hair fell freely, unbound by plaits or elastic bands.

"Good evening."

"Evening."

It was different, she was different. He entered the room with heavy steps into the room lit with a singular dull bulb. The dim lighting accentuated the few wrinkles around her green eyes. The memory of those early days had vanished with the sight of her now.

Could it be her— is it her? He wondered.

These were questions she could not answer.

He looked about the room. It was furnished and adorned with belongings too personal to be of a temporary residence. His eyes fixed for moments on objects throughout— a tall lamp with a heavy vermouth shade, a chest of drawers covered in dust with long and errant hair-strands, a case of disheveled books, and a coffee-stained bed, where a stranger, a wanderer, slept.

She turned her back on him and the door gave a loud croak upon closing. A stench of desperation diffused throughout the room with the silence that began to swell. We are what we are in silence; ineffable.

He paced forth to back, back to forth, alone in the room.

Everything began to teeter. His head was violent with noise; of misunderstandings, and of memories he wished could be undone, unfelt, unthought, unetc; of a past that could not be unreasoned.

To forgo, he thought.

He paced forth to a mirror, the disposable vanity was placed atop the chest of drawers, with stockings and cheap satin remnants of faded variety that lounged carelessly over the sides. It was a paltry view; she was, he was, they are. It was not the girl he remembered. She might have been, but she wasn't now.

He paced back to a window— The pane was lousy and cold.

Soon it will be night, where light descends and everything is a shadow, no longer reserved for dismal corners. He was famished and wanted to scavenge, and then flee; each desire surmounted the others in tormented waves of disgrace.

He paced back to the mirror, avoiding his own eye line and whispered—

"I want to unknow you."

"Hmm?" She asked and wrapped a flaccid drapery around herself. The impending darkness was cold. "Did you say something?" Her youth, gone like the desert sun.

To forget, he wished.

She nestled onto the mattress that was nearly as unkempt as she, and hovered a coffee mug in the air, balanced with grace. She extended the drink out to him. It was an offering. He watched her in the reverse reflection and shook his head, slow and decisive. She drank in the steam and the warmth of the coffee. He glanced at the books unread, unfoiled, untempted, unknown. A strand of hair fell to discard beside her and she licked the dried splatter on the coffee mug. He saw the dust begin to settle, and walked to the window, again, to check on the progression of nightfall. The steadiness of descent was undetectable— It would not be soon enough. The daylight lingered and so did she.

He looked at her, gazed and searched for something, some thing that would capture and remind him of her youth, their youth; now faded and tainted into a strange land inept of comfort but riddled with familiarity. They were now estranged and condemned as strangers. He hoped and pleaded, begged with futility for a singular grain of desert sand to appear, a remnant of times past, so that he might wake her gently again. He strained his ear in attempt to hear the Mermaid's song, but to no avail.

His mind paced back to forth, forth to back, crowded in the room. His eyes fixed for moments on objects throughout—

the coffee stained stranger;
the disheveled bed;
the books unread;
the dust to be collected;
the hairs to be brushed aside;
All to be forgotten.

Night would soon come. He saw all of this with clarity. He walked to the lamp in the same measure of the desert journey, slow and decisive, this time without need to be saved, and turned out the light. In the darkness, he sat on the mattress with a grimace, the grimace.

"I'll be back in a moment," she promised in the dark.

She slipped out from the bed, out of the room, quiet and with ginger steps. The devastation of misunderstanding had led her to wandering. She walked through the streets, still dressed with the brisk sheath of cloth. The lamps curtsied and paid salute by removing their light so as to protect the reign of darkness. The lilies, bright and white in the day, turned pale and dead in order to succumb to the darkness of the night.

The desert is an eternal summer, a land without shadow, except your own; a reminder that taunts and looms from out of the darkness and follows closely. The desert vulture is somewhere, but unseen. The cactus is perpetually alone, not to be touched.

A low hum came from her; the song of the mirage; the Mermaid's call.

And she vanished into the desert.

A Whiskey Tale

Lick the dripping coals of more
With the stiff breath of whiskey
    And Peanut shells on the floor.

Skirt the sounds of sober hours before
The red night w a n e s — as they
Lick the dripping coals of more.

To touch the ridges that contour
The earthly being mixed with complimentary
    Peanut shells on the floor

Would induce a shift in what you wore
And shed to nothing, sweet nothing— as we
Lick the dripping coals of more

The universe exists behind a closed door
Now to rest and reflect to feed the stoic effigy;
    Of Peanut shells on the floor.

If time were still the flesh toned pour
—ing sick love's tale; a spirit's blunder—
    While we Lick the dripping coals; now more
        Peanut shells on the floor.

Helena Hoar

Helena is: tea, books, more tea, purple, daughters, bed, snails, friends, more tea, proper bread, donkeys, silver, sleep, brown, cardigans, bees, boots, ale, lavender, more books, kitchen, orange, summer.

Cliff

The end of August and it was no longer possible to pretend it was summer. The rock she sat on held heat from days of sun-scorch but the light was slanting once more from autumn's direction. Her children were too inexperienced to recognise it, dipping and slipping into weedy rock pools, scraping knees on barnacles, so far into the holiday that they didn't moan when the salt stung. But she knew it and was sad.

The small embrace of beach was mostly empty. Half an hour ago a man had come down the steep slope with his dog and she had spied on him from behind her sunglasses as he walked the length of the beach, turned round and went back. The lack of people made minding the children easy. Her book butterflied on the rock beside her, but she did not care to read it. It was enough to sit and feel and listen and watch.

The gulls were noisy as they patrolled the ledges of the cliff face. Her eldest daughter Sal had tried to climb the cliff to catch one, or to pick the thrift that grew there. "Give me a leg up mummy," she had asked, grasping a rock and pulling herself up. She had discouraged her, seeing the boulders beneath and the isolation, predicting injury. She knew her phone had no signal here, and was mostly glad of that. Her daughter had argued with her then given up and wandered back to the pools.

"Come and paddle mummy," said her Kit, her youngest, and she caught her mother's hand and tugged her across the shingle down to the shore. The sea was not icy yet, and they kicked and splashed together, getting wet, the wind wrapping their hair in teeth and eyes. "I'm hungry mummy," she said. The children were always hungry on the beach. "Look! There's a boat!" said

Kit, and there was a boat, a silent, pretty boat with a white white sail, a yacht maybe. She could see people on it, lots of people jumbled on the deck, and they watched and her daughter waved. The boat was coming close now, close to the shore and she realised that it was going to anchor. The people were helping each other into a small inflatable dingy and were rowing the short distance to the beach.

It all felt too close now, there were soon going to be a dozen people striding through the waves onto the sand right next to them. "Come on!" she said to Kit, "Let's find you a sandwich." Her child was torn between hunger and intrigue. "Come on!" she urged again, and led her back towards their camp on the rocks, her daughter walking with her face still turned back towards the sea.

She listened hard, could hear the chattering and excitement of the people behind them as they dragged the dingy up the beach. They were young, she realised, and purposeful, students perhaps, their accents light in their words. She opened her bag and found a tub of sandwiches, plastic and buttery left from their lunch. Kit rammed one into her mouth with sandy fingers. The people were right behind them now, approaching the rocks, and Kit turned round and grinned at them unprettily with crusts hanging from her lips. Their mother turned too and saw they were carrying armfuls of ropes and hooks.

Her daughter, getting no reaction, let the crusts fall from her mouth and ran off to join her sister in a waist-deep pool. Her mother threw the crusts away for the gulls, but they lay shabbily on the sand. She picked up her book but did not read it. The people were so close to her now, laying down their coils of gaudy ropes on the rock a throw away from her. She wanted to move away, wanted them not to be so close to her and her heaps of bags and damp and gritty shorts and her children's buckets and spades, but did not know how. So instead she turned a page in her book.

They were organising themselves now, sorting themselves into groups. The girls among them clambered onto the rock pile next to her separated only by a pace or two of sand. They climbed up level with her then higher still and sat on the steep slant with their knees up chatting to each other. They unzipped their bright fleeces and tried to push their hair back from their pebble-smooth faces. One of the boys then scrambled easily up the cliff in front of them making the gulls squawk and flap. The boys who had gathered at the bottom of the cliff threw a rope up to him and he hammered in a hook to fasten it to the rock.

She watched, fascinated and saw her eldest daughter was watching too, jealous of the climbing. She herself was jealous of the girls, the girls who did not have to be pretty or dressed just right because they were casual in the surety of youth. The boys called and shouted and joked and worked to string a net of bright ropes and hooks from the cliff to the rock behind where she sat, testing to see if it would hold by hanging from it, suspended feet above the sand. They threw their t-shirts onto the rocks and she could see the easy muscle in their arms, their shoulders. Lithe they rigged a pulley up. And the girls just sat and watched and waited.

One of the boys acknowledged her as he passed. "Good afternoon, how are you?" he said, faltering in his step and half-raising a hand as he spoke. An old-fashioned thing to say. For a moment she was lost in the hollow of his hips, the plumped crease of flesh at the back of his neck, then she twitched a small smile at him, playing impassivity behind her sunglasses. A thought slid into her mind, *Once I fucked one as young as you,* and she clamped that thought hard in her teeth. He moved on and crouched by the girls to chat on the slope of the rock. *More than one as young as you,* she thought, *and did not relish it as I should have. Did my fingers touch muscle and skin and shoulders and arms like his? Did I lay my head on such thighs and not pleasure in it as I should have? Was I like those girls? They who are as young as children; they, so easy in their bodies, so relaxed and unassuming and waiting.* It was all so long ago she found it hard to tell.

Her children played, climbing the low part of the cliff now in imitation, and she was glad they were away from her so she could just be herself and watch without having to be a mother. And yet she knew in the stretch of fertility she could have been a mother, mother to any of these people and was it wrong that she desired them?

And there he was, the one who had spoken to her, coming back towards her again, and she lowered her book. Now he squatted down level with her and looked into her face. She raised her sunglasses because he put his face so close, so very close to hers and she saw sharp stubble, pores on his nose, smelt the sun cream and the sweat. And still he said nothing. *He is not the best-looking of them,* she thought unbidden, but she wanted to reach out and pull him close, rest her forehead on the warmth in the crook of his neck and breath deep as delight rose. He did not move or speak, but tilted his head and twinkled his clear eyes at her. *My god, is he mocking or flirting?* she thought.

"You'll have to move, or you'll be in the way," he said. And he motioned up to the ropes. One of the boys was at the high end, on the cliff, and she saw he was about to zip-wire down, over her rock and into the deep pool of water on the other side. *That is all,* she realised, *that is all, he is telling me to move.*

"I'll go then."

And slowly she gathered up a clumsy armful of clothes and towels and picked her way off the rocks, and then went back for more. She waved at her girls, and they ran to her saying, "We're not going are we mummy? We want to stay! We want to watch!"

So do I, she thought, *so do I.*

And they sat, the three together, on a blanket spread on the sand as the boys took turns to climb the cliff, slide down the rope and plummet into the pool, shouting and jeering and the girls on the rocks half-watched as they talked. But now the children said that they felt cold and she dried them off in turn with a damp and sandy towel and they protested at the roughness, and she helped them dress. She huddled her body round Kit, rubbing her chin on her hair that smelt sweet of baking biscuits. "When can I have a go mummy?" asked Sal.

"I don't think you can Sal," she said.

"But I can do it mum, I can!" Sal protested. She wondered if she would rage.

"I think they have set it up for only them to use. I don't think they'll let you have a go. When you're big like them, then you can do it."

Sal considered for a moment, and said decisively, "Let's go now." The girls ran off together up the beach and she packed up once more, calling to them to wait for her as they tumbled towards the path with their shadows long before them, and she swung the bags over her shoulder and followed.

James Postans

James is a Birmingham based writer, who is due to graduate with a BA in English and Creative Writing in September 2015. After finding a love for script writing at during his adolescence, he considers it his life goal to contribute to the official canon of *Doctor Who*.

Devon

INT. CAFÉ — DAY

ADAM carries coffee over to LOUISE.

He sits —

> LOUISE
> I was thinking about something the other
> day.

> ADAM
> Yeah? What was that?

> LOUISE
> I should get away. Go on holiday or
> something. After all the stuff with Craig,
> it just feels… right.

> ADAM
> On your own?

> LOUISE
> Maybe. Probably. Not like he would want
> to go with me anyway.

> ADAM
> I was thinking about going away too.

> LOUISE
> Where were you thinking then?

> ADAM
> Um, Italy. Italy, yeah.

> LOUISE
> Italy? That's a bit far. I was only
> thinking about Devon!

> ADAM
> Yeah, me too.

                    LOUISE
Devon's not in Italy…

                    ADAM
No, you're right. It's not. It's
definitely… not.

                    LOUISE
I was talking to a guy the other night.
He kind of put the idea in my head and,
well, I haven't managed to shake it off.

                    ADAM
Who was this then?

                    LOUISE
Just a friend. Just someone I've known
since school. Don't worry, you're still
my number one.

                    ADAM
Really? Am I?

                    LOUISE
Well, yes. Probably, I suppose. I mean,
the man of my dreams might fall our of
the sky tomorrow and knock you into
second place, let's face it.

                    ADAM
Or maybe he's already here?

                    LOUISE
Craig? Don't be stupid he's well out of
the picture now.

                    ADAM
No. Not Craig. Absolutely not Craig. I
don't know, maybe —

                    LOUISE
The other guy, the Devon guy?

                    ADAM
No, no!

                    LOUISE
Well, whoever it is, he's doing a bloody
good job of hiding away. When are you off
to Italy?

                    ADAM
I'm not going to Italy.

                    LOUISE
You said you were —

                    ADAM
I said I was thinking about it?

                    LOUISE
So, when are you thinking about going to
Italy?

                    ADAM
When are you thinking about going to
Devon?

                    LOUISE
You're doing it again. You're going all
grumpy. You're pulling that face you
pull when you go grumpy.

                    ADAM
I don't pull a face.

                    LOUISE
Yes, yes you do. It's all. Crinkly and
grumpy. Just a grumpy - a very grumpy
face.

                    ADAM
I'm really not grumpy. How could I be
grumpy when I'm around you?

                    LOUISE
And what does that mean?

                    ADAM
That means… If you decide to go to Devon,
and that other guy doesn't want to go
with you, you don't need to go alone.

                        LOUISE
              It's not exactly Italy…

                         ADAM
              It doesn't need to be.

                        LOUISE
              We've been through this.

                         ADAM
              I know. I'm sorry. But I can't -

                        LOUISE
              You're my best friend, Adam… I'm sorry
              but I'm not prepared to lose that. You'll
              always be there. This other guy… This
              other guy probably won't.. when he does
              go, you're going to be sitting there
              with your coffee, listening to me rattle
              on. So, yeah, you're my number one guy
              because... Because you stick by me when
              they don't. So, if I decide to go to
              Devon with him, you promise me that
              you'll be here when I come back, yeah?

                         ADAM
              Yeah, of course I promise.

They smile and sip coffee.

FADE TO BLACK.

Alan Jarvis

Alan is currently studying an English and Creative Writing course, while praying to secure some kind of consistent employment through screenwriting or fiction in the future. He is bridging these precious carefree years in between by writing his first fantasy novel amidst pub and gaming sessions.

Deep Dark

Dan bolted awake and collapsed on the cockpit dashboard, crunching most of the buttons and illuminating the powered-down satellite interior. He flicked them all back and snapped the radio headphones over his head, wincing as he filtered out the whine of interference and discerned a vaguely-familiar voice.

"Dan? Help – Dan?"

Dan opened his mouth to speak but instead he produced a hoarse cough. It had been a long time since he had spoken to anyone.

"Yes? It's Dan. Who's this? Command?"

"It's John. Your contact. I've left my airlock and I'm approaching your satellite now. I assume you'll need some assistance, judging from how you're too lazy to answer the comm?"

"John?"

"Yes... Remember me? I was due to help resupply you on this mission. It's been nine months."

"Right. Yeah, of course. I'll open the airlock for you."

Dan gazed into the darkness of space as he stood on the underside of his satellite. He had occupied most of his spare time inside admiring the view but it was different being out on the hull, being able to switch off the magnets in his boots and drift out into the void with the flip of a switch. He felt exposed, vulnerable, as if the stars were watching him.

"Dan, I've removed the panel – stop panicking and help me."

Dan lowered his gaze from the stark vista to the grey hull of the satellite and turned slowly, his boots sucking on the metal like a sticky floor.

"I wasn't panicking," he said.

John motioned to the opened hatch before him with a hand-held drill, revealing circuit boards and grey tubing.

"I didn't say you were. Now, come on."

Dan knelt down by the opened hatch, staring in to a web of wiring, and realized that he had no idea what he was supposed to do.

"We have to re-route the secondary systems back through the main computer, Dan."

"Uh, yeah, I know."

"Are you feeling okay?" asked John.

"I'm feeling a little light-headed, to be honest. I haven't been outside for a while."

John parted the top layer of wiring like a pair of curtains to reveal a glowing circuit-board beneath.

"We can take it slow, Dan, we haven't got much time-"

Dan rose to his feet and took a sluggish step back, staring down at John until he turned around.

"What?"

"We've got plenty of time," snapped Dan. "I've been here for nine months, being drugged every twelve hours, and I haven't sworn once, but if you contradict yourself again I'm going to break that record – copy that?"

John glanced him up and down a few times and barked a short, sharp laugh.

"Copy. Come on, let's sort this out and we can get you back on board. I don't want to have to report a serious case of cabin fever to NASA on this new project, am I? The hell are they drugging you with, anyway?"

"Some kind of tame hallucinogenic, like a social experiment in space, seeing whether or not it boosts productivity, I guess," muttered Dan, peering back into the exposed circuitry and brandishing the drill, as if he knew what he was doing. "Maybe they're having a kind of side-affect, I don't know. It's like I've never seen one of these systems before."

John pulled him away from the hatch and sat down on the hull, staring out into the blackness, and motioned for Dan to join him.

"You should report this to Command, they need to know about glitches in their project."

"Perhaps it's not a glitch, perhaps it's just me – the drugs react to my subconscious."

"How do you know I'm not a result of it, then?" asked John.

"Well, I tried to think up a woman a few months back, just to see if it would work, you know? If all it brought me was you then that's definitely a glitch that needs fixing!"

John laughed gruffly at this, making Dan's in-helmet radio crackle.

"You're wondering how I knew about your experiment, aren't you?" asked John after a moment. "Now you're trying to bring up my NASA profile in your head, trying to understand how I'd know that. This is a one-man mission. The big corporates only need one casualty in case it all goes belly up, right? And we're just past the days of sending dogs and monkeys up, you know? They want some genuine feedback. Where's that NASA profile, then? You know, the one you would've checked to see who you would be working with on this mission – that's if there was even room for two on this tiny piece of driftwood?"

The silence was like a fog inside his helmet as he waited for something more, more explanation to rumble through his radio. Dan slowly rose to his feet and stepped back as John continued to sit, staring out into the darkness.

"Where did you say you parked your ship?" whispered Dan thickly.

"Yeah..." murmured John, smiling thinly. "The human mind has ways of coping with stress, pain, trauma, even life-threatening situations." Dan turned and stomped silently along the hull towards the aft-side airlock but John's voice continued to fill his helmet through the radio, even though Dan pushed every button on the arms of his space-suit. "You are experiencing one of those situations right now. And so am I, believe it or not. You know my name because you know me, but not here and now, not this version of me..."

Dan reached the airlock. He rotated the circular handle clockwise, and the doors slid open. He climbed inside, closing the doors behind him, waited for the red-lit airlock to pressurize, then removed his helmet. John's revelations had ceased and Dan crumpled against the airlock wall in relief, breathing deeply. It took him a few minutes to muster the energy to exit the airlock, walking just as sluggishly and zombie-like as he had been on the hull, stripping off his suit and leaving the components in the steel corridor behind him. He staggered into the satellite cockpit and collapsed in the leather armchair, or whatever this narcotic-frenzy could conjure. He did not care. He pulled his beloved shawl which he had left slung over the back of the chair tight around his body, his grey t-shirt drenched with a cold sweat. He was shaking violently.

"You're an astronaut who doesn't even know how to do basic rewiring!"

Dan bolted upright. With shaking fingers he picked up the radio headset from the floor and lifted it to one ear.

"The perfect escape – left alone in solitude, away from danger, where you can change your surroundings when you want, or rather, when you *need* to – to forget the hellish situation you are really in," informed John. Dan angrily snapped the headset cord, but John's voice crackled down from the overhead speakers in the cockpit: "I *am* a result of your subconscious. All of this is. Did you seriously believe any of this? Drugs in space? You wish! I know what you're thinking – I'm just a software glitch, some kind of fault in the project. You are so confused, so distraught, in such shock and agony, you simply locked up – retreated inside of your own mind – where nothing really makes sense, but you ignore it because deep down you don't want to get out of here. I am the only thing which is offering a sensible explanation and you are trying to ignore me."

"Right, right – okay, right – just what the hell – is going on?" hissed Dan, tears prickling his eyes like hot needles. "What is this? Who are you?"

"I'm with you right now. I have been all along. You've been here for something closer to a week, probably, not nine months. I'm trying to wake you up. You'll be given your dose soon and then God knows when I'll next be able to break through like this."

"The hallucinogens?" Dan gazed up at the black disc above his head, then glanced at his watch: "seven minutes until the next one? We weren't on the hull for more than half an hour!"

"Time is all relative, Dan," crackled John through the speakers, "time jumps around in dreams, this is no different. Listen closely; the things in this place, in this subconscious of yours, they mean something, they relate to their counterpart in the real world!"

"I don't know – I don't understand-" whimpered Dan.

"The disc on the ceiling – you're tied up somewhere, and you are being given regular doses of poison to keep you sedated, draining you – and your mind is translating it into a drug-dispenser. Translating all of your pain into this. A childhood dream."

"Tied up?"

"So am I. The real me. We both are."

Eventually, "I feel weird."

"Good. That means you're waking up."

Dan was thrown to the cockpit floor. He scrambled for purchase as his legs were lifted up in a sudden shrieking vortex of wind. Dan twisted around and saw that the front of the cockpit had gone, torn open as if by a giant hand. The leather armchair was sucked out into the vacuum of space in a cloud of swirling metal debris – stuttering back into its true form, no more than a grey plastic stand. Alarms wailed, the cockpit flashed red and

Dan's grip was relinquished as the section of floor he clung desperately to peeled upwards like a pencil shaving in a sharpener. Spinning, he glimpsed the walls of the satellite blast outwards into space. He did not even know what he was managing to hold on to, and almost on cue the drug-dispenser came away from the ceiling, striking Dan in the face. He was launched backwards, out of the disintegrating satellite, perhaps waking up like John theorized, perhaps dying like he still believed.

The last thing he heard, its proximity unknown in the spinning darkness was the drug-dispenser beginning to hiss, preparing to deliver its medicine.

Amy Wong

Amy is currently a second year student studying BA (Hons) English. She has loved reading from a young age. Some of her favourite authors are John Green, Anny Cassidy, Malorie Blackman, and Sarah Dessen.

The Ghost of You

That day I saw you,
I'll never forget.
How you made me feel,
I hope you regret.

The empty silence between us,
Not knowing what to say.
After everything we had been through,
You just walked away.

They say time is a healer,
They weren't wrong there.
All I want to know is...
Did you even care?

Lost in Thought

Below are specks of dust
scattered.
A magical scenery of flickering lights.

Soaring through the sky,
disappearing into the night.

Floating above the clouds,
drifting away.
A new day awakens
as the sun makes its appearance.

Softly landing
with paradise waiting.

Olivia Hodgson

Olivia Hodgson is a day dreamy, 20-year-old English and Creative Writing student from Birmingham. She is influenced by a broad range of authors and styles, experimenting with the snapshots of short fiction and poetry. Olivia wishes to pursue studying literature to PhD level, as well as teach English and continue volunteering in Morocco. She is currently looking to work for a local theatre company and listens to too much Morrissey.

Afternoon

I remember exactly the way you left the house: your careful stride, straight as an ignition key, then the sharp clip of familiar shoes on flagstones as you approached me. The Italian car pressed against my hip as I leaned; pushing us together towards our afternoon.

The silent ivory house, like those in Kinkade paintings, let you leave for me without restraint. The hulking home of generations was circled, not quite enclosed, by the blooming Warwickshire overgrowth; half emerging from the willows and redcurrant bushes, peaking at us through its windows. I admired your height: your brow the same height as beams slicing through your house, keeping it upright and living.

The sunlight's flash off the metal 'GT' badge reminded me of the glint through your slender framed glasses. Bowing my head to enter the car, I let my hair fall over my shoulder and created a temporary curtain between us. A few intricate silver dials adorned the dashboard like clockwork cogs nestled on bark. The bonnet's paint, the colour of bitten lips, cut a line across the scattered tufts of branches that drew the horizon. The possibilities were placed before me, hanging like each petal of the apple blossom that spotted the car in shade, not quite allowing the rays to strike the metal body. I glanced at you through my hair, comfortable in your capsule. Your gaze, unlike my reluctance, held.

I wanted to tell you; I just wasn't sure how to express it at the time. I went to draw breath in an attempt to stitch together my thoughts without them perceived as inadequate clichés. Your lips gently curved into a smile, analysing my features as I noticed the patch on your chin you had missed while shaving. The speck-led sparks in my nerves were covered for now. I settled back into the warm wool of a jacket separating my bare shoulders from the creased leather seat. You started the engine; petrol thrum-ming through the pipes, like blood creeping though atriums and ventricles.

Richard Hughes

Richard is a second-year mature student at Birmingham City University studying English and Creative Writing. In addition to the written word, he also writes songs under the name 'Gulag Gumbo' and plays mandolin in the 'Midnight Bonfires'.

Between Wind and Water

Between Wind and Water, that part of a ship's side which is now in, now out of, the water owing to the fluctuation of the waves: in a vulnerable or precarious place or position.

(Chambers Twentieth Century Dictionary)

The Birmingham air imbibes a neutral smell having grown up amidst it. According to Professor Barry C Smith, co-director and founder of the Centre for the Study of the Senses, "Studies have shown that people who lose their sense of smell end up more severely depressed and for longer periods of time than people who go blind." Perhaps, as opposed to something as overtly and instantly catastrophic as the loss of one's sight, the loss of taste is of a gnawing quality and can gradually cause one to become unstable. The denial of total stimulation, I believe, is one of the roots of human unhappiness. We live in a deadened state, pacified. We are our own animal: we cage ourselves; or we flay ourselves and lord our skin in front of us as a shield. It is why I once felt I could only function well socially with alcohol; because alcohol is the adhesive that brings the skin back to the body, reconnects the nerves, and allows the freedom of being wrong. Alcohol is Birmingham's favourite scapegoat. Until we manage to harness the courage and sociability of alcohol we are doomed to a reclusive existence, living among the purgatorial air, of which only the temperature changes: in warm weather it becomes harder to breath; it condenses and sweats in your lungs. The cold air is bearable; the colder the better. For life in Birmingham to survive it needs to be in permanent stasis. If the organism is thawed, it moulds and reeks before dying.

As I descend into the One Stop shopping centre in Perry Barr I am possessed by such a profound listlessness that it requires the force of my feet, at the command of the dull progression of the escalator, hitting the immovable floor to propel me, like an unimpeded object through a vacuum, across the floor that resembles a mundane mosaic. The floor particularly troubles me as it seems to be the one attempt at creativity. I am swallowed into a drab delirium in which the fictitious interior designer I have created in my mind, young and fresh-faced, full of originality and authenticity, is continuously quashed by his contemporaries and superiors to the point that, upon seeing his compromised design brought into reality, he commits self-murder.

As I walk into the car park, encompassed by the monoliths of consumerism, I notice that the roof of the amalgamated structures is the same lead dusted, paper-white, as the sky; the division is scarcely distinguishable, as though the pitiful pop-history of the 21st Century has been grafted onto the natural earth by some deft plastic surgeon.

I walk the circumference of the car park. I check my pockets: phone, keys, wallet. I turn to check I have not dropped something on the pavement behind me - I have not. In doing so, I recognise a writer-friend of mine, a young Hindu-Punjabi man with a dark and enigmatic past. He is on my Creative Writing course at Birmingham City University, and I concede, is one of the few writers on the course that I am jealous of. We discuss the stage around us, meticulously attempting to unravel the knotted gossamer threads of cliché and describe our concrete-marshland home. He draws our conversation to an ambulance on the far side of the car park. Our consciousness' now sit above the emergency vehicle, attempting to describe it uniquely, as our outer babushka dolls remain unmoving, save for the actions required by speech. He describes it as lemon-yellow. I become excited due to the fact I work in a fruit shop – because he is referencing an aspect of my life or I feel I may have the chance to one-up him, I do not know. I counter that instead of lemon the colour of the ambulance is more similar to that of the paled limes I sometimes find amongst a box of visually healthier chlorophyll-green limes. That I considered the pale limes to be not healthy and that I used that colour to describe an ambulance resonates with me briefly. However, before I get the chance to develop that thought further I become aware that I do not know why certain limes arrive at the shop where I work are paler than others. A few theories come to mind: under ripe, bleached by the sun, neglected crop. The fact that I am unsure reinforces in me that I am not an expert in anything, even my work. It feels that I am constantly being schooled by others. Even on the rare occasions I find myself talking with confidence on a subject I tend to be overcome. Either I become aware that I am conversing well and subsequently stall, or I begin to feel detached from my listener and that I am dull, or I become aware of the precariousness of my elevated position and suffer such profound vertigo that it leads me to step down from the podium. I become embarrassed and drop the subject of pale limes before my friend asks how they come to be. We walk together, slowly, trying to notice things. He completes my first lap of the complex with me and then disbands. I watch him ascend via the elevator before beginning another circuit.

If I pay attention to the sound around me it becomes unbearable: the crowds and their voices and their footfalls and their motorised buggies and their cars and their chewing and their spit and their digestion. Unable to differentiate between the multitudinous code, I feel the pressure mount between my ears to the point that I have to waggle my lobe and move my jaw. I begin to feel anxious and I begin to think of AIDS and then I try to satiate my anxiety with mantra:

1. You have been tested.
2. You left the correct amount of incubation period needed for accurate test results.
3. All the tests came back negative.
4. You are all clear.
5. Everything is fine.

I repeat this four times. I have an urge to repeat it again but I realise if I do that it will become hard to stop until I become exhausted by it because it is hard to figure out a truly safe number after four. Ten would work but it is hard to ascertain if the count is still valid at a number that large.

Once I have calmed down I feel guilty as I have once again resorted to my old ways of coping with anxiety. *Overcoming Obsessive Compulsive Disorder*, an extremely insightful text that is helping me to understand and cure my disorder, uses a metaphor to describe the treatment of OCD: when you find yourself in a deep hole, blindfolded, and your only tool is a shovel, you have to drop the shovel to search for a different way out; the ladder that the book will provide. I seem to be constantly placating my recovery, insisting one last time, or claiming it is not worth the risk and resorting back to the ritual. I am constantly dropping the shovel, then panicking and blindly scrambling for it again. I know it is nonsensical. This is why I infuriate myself so.

Through self-analysis, I believe my OCD began when I was about sixteen. This is not unusual in men - who tend to develop it in their late teens. I remember having a fascination for tortured minds; the onset of my OCD felt like a reaction to this. This resulted in me struggling with feelings of inauthenticity regarding my mental health problem. However, this was probably not the root cause. As an example, religious people who follow regular rituals can have OCD; but religion does not directly cause OCD. In the words of Veale and Willson in *Overcoming Obsessive*

Compulsive Disorder, 'if you had been brought up in a different culture, you would probably have developed a different form of OCD.' This comforted me. It said to me that having a fascination with tortured minds did not mean that I artificially gave myself OCD; I would have got it anyway. It legitimised my illness for me and confirmed that I needed to do something about it. The trigger event – OCD has been known to achieve fruition through a trauma – was probably my first sexual experience, which I bungled. The wait to confirm that I had not accidentally got her pregnant was distressing. The queasy uneasiness of the wait that I experienced then sometimes returns to me now and I worry that I have accidentally hurt someone or done something wrong. This leads to the rituals I perform in the hope of sanctifying myself and preventing catastrophe.

As I continue my loop I wonder whether any of my anguish has manifested itself outwardly. I occasionally notice the contortions of my face; these mental relays sometimes lead me to grimace. I worry that those urban ramblers, observational poets, my kin, might look upon me and despise me, believing that I grimace at the world.

On my third lap of the complex I begin to think about a musician-friend of mine who recently began experiencing bouts of anxiety. We had walked his dog – a lean, retired greyhound – around the back roads of Moseley village. He had been giving himself a hard time because of this new phenomena he was experiencing, something that he associated with weakness, and had only just begun to ease off and look at himself, not only objectively, but compassionately as well. It seems to me that men, from childhood, are indoctrinated to dismiss and curse their fallibility. This in turn leads to larger problems; problems that would have remained the same size and even shrunk with communication. One does not leave cancer to grow; why do we insist on doing so with our anxiety? However, there is also, with men, a problem validating if there is something wrong as they are less inclined than women to seek help or even consult a doctor for advice. Remembering my friend – talented, witty, good looking, strong minded, the sort of person one imagines to have a perfect, almost animated, control of life – talking candidly that night about his anxiety, I feel compelled to respond to my own mental health problem in a healthier manner. I should not be ashamed. I should seek help. I should call Birmingham Healthy Minds. I start to think that perhaps this revelation is enough, that I should not waste their time. But then I remember the ease with which I slide back into old habits and I become resolved to make the effort.

And then it becomes frightfully clear that it is all about effort. Whether we are our own individual gods or merely – and I use the world 'merely' somewhat tenuously – the neurons that make up the consciousness of a singular God; effort on our own part is essential. As Ghandi said:

'Whatever you do will be insignificant, but it is very important that you do it.'

It seems to me that there is an internal human battle afoot. Similar to the metaphorical battle of light and dark; but of course light and dark are not in conflict as they are not conscious, they are only responding to our universe's natural laws. The battle wages between the forces of effort: those attempting self-betterment, charity and the progression of understanding and consciousness; and the forces of lethargy: those that opt for an unimpeded decline and wont for euthanasia of consciousness as a whole – blissful nothingness. Permeating this intrinsic battle waged by all mankind is its own epiphenomenon; the fluctuating, 'happiness and sadness spectrum'. Effort and lethargy need to learn to cohabit in order for happiness to succeed. Where there is division there is unhappiness; there is also unhealthy one-sidedness. The differences are fine and should be expected, but so far they have not been accepted by all.

Happiness and sadness, such simple notions, but of course the simplest notions are the most beautiful. Unfortunately, repetition has caused us to become accustomed to them. In Futurama, when Philip J Fry, at the end of the universe, asks the professor what the meaning of life is, the professor replies: 'Who knows? Probably some hogwash about the human spirit.'

The human spirit; the big cliché. But of course it was once not cliché. Once, it was said and it was understood. Now, the notion is as mundane as One Stop's floor. But, of course, it is not mundane in the least. It is a fine work, forever incomplete, save for when we are annihilated – and even then it will occupy its own grand and terrible time in space. When we become extinct, God dies; as God is either our creation or we are God attempting to understand itself. God can either die with grace and old age or euthanize itself, leaving the universe alone and unperceived. It requires effort. The human spirit needs to be reworded so it can be properly seen and understood afresh.

On my final lap of the shopping complex, I witness a bird attacking disregarded pastry-goods, just inside by the sliding doors, as a woman records it on her mobile phone. I find the scene oddly pornographic. Subsequently, I become ashamed by my own act of voyeurism. As I turn away, a child releases a black balloon. I follow its journey up to the rafters, my eyes a little unfocused, and shiver as it bounces off what I imagine to be a pair of feet belonging to my mind's interior designer; feet that turn slowly this way and slowly that and slowly back again.

Additional Notes

'Between Wind and Water' phrase.
Chambers Twentieth Century Dictionary, (Edinburgh: W & R Chambers Ltd, 1978) p. 1561
Taste and Smell: What is it like to live without them? Denise Winterman. BBC News Magazine.29.06.2013 http://www.bbc.co.uk/news/magazine-23051270

Veale, David, and Rob Willson, *Overcoming Obsessive Compulsive Disorder: A self-help guide using Cognitive Behavioral Techniques* (UK: Constable & Robinson Ltd, 2005)

Health and Health Service: *Use of Services and Social Variations.* Department of Health, Social Services and Public Safety. http://www.dhsspsni.gov.uk/health_service_use_ni8.pdf

Danielle Mason

Danielle Mason is a 20-year-old BA English student who has recently found her calling for creative writing. Although Danielle has welcomed and accepted her calling, she is still queen of procrastination and sits at her desk whilst the Ryman's A4 paper screams at her, 'Danielle, I know you want to, stroke me with your creativity, cover me in words, put pen to paper and start writing'... but it rarely happens.

The First Day of December

The first day of December starts on a Monday. Typical.

The first day of the worst month in the year starts on the worst possible day. The next thirty days cannot come quickly enough. The frost has set in and the morning dew is dripping from the chipped front room windows. I wake up and traipse down the stairs with my hair askew, my dressing gown half off my shoulders carrying a cold cup of tea in my right hand. I can see my own breath when I sigh to myself and start thinking about the upcoming month. In twenty four days the old, fat, bearded bastard is going to sell dreams to my children. Brilliant.

This Morning have already predicted that the school grey sleet will arrive tomorrow. Great. The first day of bad weather, always leads to one thing, *West Midlands Travel* coming to a festive stand still because of the episodic weather. Perfect.

"I'm afraid to say love, that Corsa in't fit to be on the road. It's failed the MOT and the brake fluid is leakin' again. I'm sorry, I know it's not what you want t' hear so close t' Christmas. I'd rather not have to be the one telling you. Sorry, love." As lovely and comforting as Bill, my mechanic, is trying to be in his great Northern accent this is literally the last thing I need. I haven't got the patience to take the kids on the bus and a taxi is completely out of the question.

I hate winter as much as I hate when Shelly from Greggs tries to serve me cold sausage rolls at 9 o'clock on a Wednesday morning. Unbelievable. They're supposed to be fresh out of the oven. I want to take a bite and see the pastry crumble on to my two-day old shirt. I want to feel the grease graze my taste buds and settle on the corners of my mouth. What I don't want is to taste freezing cold horse meat dressed up as 100% British pork.

I asked Scott and Charley to write their Christmas letters to Him on Saturday morning to keep them entertained while I made a pathetic attempt to clean up after the week's events. Bloody hell, who knew two kids could be so messy? Once they had finished writing them in their neatest possible handwriting and they had drowned the second class stamps in saliva, they begged me to post them as soon as possible. But instead, I had to tell them that Santa would only accept letters posted after the first of December, and that I would post them on the way to work on Monday. Once I had sent them into their room to finish designing their sleighs, I had to break my promise of posting letters, and I had to cut around the stamps popping them back into my faux leather purse. I then put the letters on top of the wardrobe in my bedroom, out of the twins reach so I'd know they would be safe. Neither of them are ready to face the truth about Santa and I'm not ready to face the heartbreak I'll be inflicting by telling them he's not real. They've suffered enough already this year and I refuse to put them through any more. As it's just the three of us this year, I have to make it one of the best Christmases they've ever had.

With the boys soundly asleep in their bunk beds with matching Ben 10 duvets, I took their letters from on top of the wardrobe and into the bathroom. I opened them sitting crossed legged on the floor with my Mayfair Superking rolling between my fingers, naughtily tapping ash in the toothbrush holder. Even though they are identical, my eight year old twins have completely different personalities. Scott, quite clearly the extrovert, has asked for an iPad Air, an Xbox Connect with at least three games, a brand of trainers I've never heard of, Lego, a NERF Gun, colouring pens and pencils, Frozen on Blu- Ray and a pair of singing Christmas snowman socks. Tears slowly fall from the corners of my eyes as I carefully open the second letter from Charley, my practical and introverted son. His letter simply states: 'Dear

Santa, hope you and Mrs Clause are well. This year all I would like for Christmas is for my Mommy and Daddy to get back together so we can be a real family again. Love Charley, aged 8 and 1/4.' But then at the bottom of the letter 'P.S I still want everything Scott asked for'. Well shit. I already know who won't be getting almost any of these.

While I'm having to reuse Aldi's extra value tea bags, my boys are dreaming of the world. Where I used to be able to give the twins three pounds a day for school, I've had to sign them up for free school dinners and that 'no longer includes a drink' according to the letter I got from the school secretary. I have always been in competition with their father. Chris could buy them anything and possibly everything they wanted on their Christmas list and it certainly wouldn't be a problem.

He was always the twins' favourite and I was always the one standing on the side-lines in the rain carrying their muddy football boots while the three of them ran off to the car to listen to the latest One Direction song on a Sunday afternoon. On the first of December, if the boys had school Chris would always have half a day off from work so he would be able to pick them up once he had finished. Then he would take them for a chicken nugget Happy Meal with strawberry milkshakes. Once they came home, he would climb into the loft and take out the three massive boxes of Christmas decorations and the boys would spend all night making the house look like Santa's grotto. They would always wait for me to come home from work before putting the last and final piece on the tree, our Christmas fairy. The boys Christmas would start at that exact moment, when the tree lights would turn on and I would always go and make us hot chocolates with marshmallows as an extra special treat.

Chris and I went to Barbados for our honeymoon. The flight was a disaster. I'd never flown before and so we started our two-week celebration of love with an eight hour flight full of panic and Virgin branded sick bags. Romantic. After our disastrous honeymoon, everyone knew that it was Chris's job to go up the ladder. It was his job to brave climbing up the unstable, chipped wooden steps to go into the loft. It was his job to start Christmas with the boys and to be the fun parent. The only job he had to do was be their favourite.

"Mom," my twins say in unison.

"It's the first of December," Scott follows.

"I know."

"You know what the first of December means, don't you?" Charley continues.

"I do."

"It means it's the first day of Christmas," says Scott.

"I know."

"It's nearly time to go to McDonalds..." spoken by Charley.

"...And take down the decorations," Scott says finishing his brother's sentence.

I sigh.

"Is dad coming to take us? We do it every year." Charley states in a matter of fact tone.

I sigh again, but this time louder hoping they get the message. I hope they stop before they begin the chorus of 'moms'. They know it gets on my last nerve.

"Mom...mom...mommy...mom.."

If I squeeze my eyes together tight enough I can barely hear them. I try to imagine I'm on a private island with a stiff vodka in my hands and not sitting on my worse-for-wear sofa with my hands massaging my temples.

"MOM!"

That's it. As my temperature rises, so does my voice. "Charley, Scott, I am totally aware of what day it is. I know that this was your day with your father but he is not here and you've got to get used to it. Both of you are doing my head in, with your stupid questions, get to your room. Now."

I look up at my children as they hand in hand, sprint up the stairs. Both sniffing back tears. Oh God, what have I done? If I had to choose between my life and theirs, I would die for my children and I need to start showing it.

To calm myself down, I light up and take a long pull. Before I know it I'm on my third and last cigarette. Shit. I try to pull myself together. Things aren't the same but I still want to make this the best Christmas I can; for the twins.

I walk into the kitchen and pour myself a shot of neat whiskey in a streaked stained Transformers Prime plastic cup. I never used to like alcohol; a lot of what we have was whatever Chris had left. All the same, I down it in one and pour myself another for courage. It's got to be done.

I slowly drag my mobile out of my pocket and send a quick text to Chris, telling him he needs to come and collect the twins. Within minutes I get a reply that makes my stomach flip.

'ALREADY ON MY WAY, B @ UR's IN 5 MINS BBE X'

I don't reply, nor do I communicate with him as he uses his keys to come in and get the kids ready for McDonalds. I stand in the kitchen pretending to wash up this morning's dishes and I go to the door and watch them as they leave. None of them look at me and nobody even attempts to say goodbye as they pass over the threshold. They just shut the door behind them.

I decide not to waste any more time. I drag the ladders across the landing and place them against the loft door, shaking it twice checking for safety. I look up to the ceiling as a knot forms in the pit of my stomach and the tears begin to roll down my face. I can do this. I grip the ladders with both hands until they go crimson, willing myself to just go up and start Christmas. I put my left foot on the bottom step, take a breath and carry on to the next. With each step I pluck up the courage to go further, all the while the knot in my stomach threatens to drag me down. If I look at the floor beneath me, I'll vomit all over the cream, paisley carpet. I've got to keep going to prove to my children that even though their mother is on her own, I can still give them the life they had with their father here... I can provide for them, cook for them, clean up after them and make all of their Christmas wishes come true.

Back in the living room with a fresh cup of tea in my hand, I flick through the channels with my legs pulled up to my stomach when I hear the key in the lock.

CLICK.

Prem Mehra

Prem is currently studying Creative Writing at Birmingham City University. At his desk, he has characters clamped down between the lines and performs nocturnal brain surgeries. Prem is enraptured by the blood that spills out on the page, and the pen that orchestrates the mess for people to view.

Icarus

The Christmas period: I'm at Royal Mail, on the main floor, sorting letters into pigeonholes. Machines gargle leaden trays packed with letters, moving across their lolled, corrugated tongues. They stop to masticate for several moments at a time, before spitting them out, like a mouthful of feathers.

I pick up an A5 postcard (and when my line manager isn't around), I feel it over. A slice of life. I turn it over and read; this is when I peer into people's lives with cheap binoculars - I see only the outside, the frayed, blurry edges. I run a finger along the words embossed into the postcard, trace the emotion, imagine the people behind the ink, learn them. Big letters meant someone carefree, perhaps unabashed. A free spirit. Small letters? Restricted, maybe a prissy individual. I even lie the postcard flat in my palm, searching for a peculiar weight. At times I do think that I find one; or it's simply a phantom.

Yes, a phantom.

Leaning forward and hunched over the desk with my elbows propped on a pile of unsorted letters, I read postcards. I come across descriptions of the vast lands of New Zealand; the delightful weather in Sydney; or incomprehensible paragraphs of hanzi. I stare at the fronts, the aerial shots of coral reefs and pale blue lagoons, shimmering in a different moment in time. I look round the edges for an end to the seas in these pictures but see none. My binocular images remain unfocused. I pause for a moment and look up to the ceiling. Nothing but a warren of grating with thick, cylindrical silver pipes running along them like breathing tubes keeping the place ventilated. My eyes back down to the postcards in my hands. The lives in these bits of cards aren't phantoms.

I'm distracted by a metallic bang that reverberates along my grid of pigeonholes. A Christmas casual is seated to my right, her set of pigeonholes next to mine, and I watch nimble flashes of her outstretched jazz hands, chucking in post that slams against the back. The vibration shivers across to my workstation. I'm just one member of two lines of lime, hi-viz clad individuals with our backs to each other sorting Birmingham post; it was also how the line managers identified the casual workers from the permanent, red hi-viz staff. I swivel round on my seat and watch other casuals: one nods her head in rhythm to music whispering from her earphones, while others relay jokes to each other, spinning on stools and guffawing, a sheaf of post bulging in the grip of their gloved hands.

The line manager walks into view, head low and hands interlocked behind his back as though in meditation. Our eyes meet. Before I can turn back to work, he hollers at me. He waves his stubby hand, and puckers his brow.

I'm a step behind him as he takes me across the floor; I stare at the lattice of filiform hair bundled on the grooves of his left ear. He stops and points at large trollies - called yorks - stacked with trays, and piles of sorted mail on stands. He explains that he wants me to put X with Y then take it out with Z. He leaves. My eyes dart about the mess. I try to process the instructions.

4:30am: six hours into my shift and I'm in the canteen with a cup of hot chocolate in hand. I'm on my fifteen-minute break before the final stretch of my shift. My back is stiff. I'm surrounded by empty chairs and unoccupied tables wiped clean. A repeat of the BBC morning news coverage drones from a HDTV in a square section of the canteen, lined with armchairs filled with bleary-eyed employees. I'm slumped in my chair, away from volumes of other hi-viz jackets. The notion of hi-viz jackets makes me think that we're highlighted as life's outcasts. I think about how

I ended up here, in this situation. Sip. The hot chocolate feels like friction burn in my mouth. I can't taste the sugar. Maybe I've built up a resistance.

Or it may be that I am desensitised to things that I loathe, that irk me beyond measure but nonetheless I keep a straight, pliant face: a cursory smile, a meek bow of the head. Silence. Silence is better. I'm adept at not moving my lips, letting others talk while I sit in the background.

However, years ago I could've rambled on about the brain.

I put the cup down when I notice something on my palms. They're covered in dirt, ingrained in flexion creases, and in whorls and arches of my fingertips. I had forgotten to ask for gloves. This is not the life that I had promised myself – a life I cussed when I was younger and naïve.

They were meant to be the hands of a surgeon, not a labourer's.

The thought was festering, to kill myself.

My eyes were ripped red-raw, no more tears flowing. My head throbbed and my nose leaked with clear strings of snot collecting on my shirt. In one hand I held a manila envelope, a sticker attached to its front that bore my name and address, and in the other, the folded OCR and AQA sheets of my A-Level results. It was August. Time massaged my shortcomings into my head.

The college head of science, Yaseen Shahid, his grey eyes and crooked nose now more vivid than in reality, flashed in my mind's eye as I sat on the edge of my bed looking out of the window.

"You won't get into medicine," he declared.

It was the college open day, and I'd been referred to him by a member of staff once my lofty ambitions and GCSE grades failed to reconcile.

"Tell me why I should allow you on the A-Level course."

I thought up a cliché as he looked down at me. 'I believe I have the enthusiasm to push myself and make this happen.'

I expected to take on the world with this answer, this ambition that sent my heart in a flutter and kept my footsteps light and head up to the sky. Instead, the hubbub of other prospective students, and teachers sliding paperwork into folders continued, unaffected.

So was the head of science, who laughed, gripped his chin, and continued to peruse my results' sheets. "Okay," he said. "I'll make you a conditional offer."

There were myriad stipulations to his acceptance of my position on the course.

Sometime later I told my eldest brother: "You just watch. I'll work my ass off like never before. I won't be resting."

4:45am: the doors of the canteen flip behind me as if shooing me away while I walk back to the floor. I push a blue door and the silence dies at the threshold, mini yorks clattering, their brakes snapping them into movement, managers yelling orders – all balling up like a bit of gum. I'm the first one back to my work station. I regard the three-winged sets of pigeonholes tagged with strips of laminated paper marked with postcodes. Bromsgrove. Redditch. Great Barr. I look at the coloured tongues of post sticking out at me from pigeonholes. I shake my head. I can't live an unremarkable life, shoved into a mundane slot that'll fizzle out without recognition. I have to escape. Transcend.

I remember reading a neuroscience book I have at home, locked away...

I see my line manager strolling about. I walk up to him, ask if I can have gloves. I exhibit the dirt by turning my hands over.

...You see, I was going to become the greatest neurosurgeon since Benjamin Carson. I'll sign autobiographies. I'll retire and die with the world appreciating my existence, knowing that I saved lives. That I was God.

He places a hand on my shoulder, crinkles his face and nods, tells me he'd see, then directs me to another place to work.

My third year of A-levels. A retake year. I had suffered enough of my brother's verbal jabs by then ('I thought you was going to work your ass off?'). I was in the college library, signed in to my email account, eyes roving over the list of emails. I had enquired at the University of Birmingham a few days prior about whether they accepted retake students.

I re-read the bold subject line of an email: Ref 13/21555: Medical School admissions query.

The cursor highlighted the email and became a hand, its finger pointed. But I scrolled away. I tended to other emails, then came back to the same one. I clicked.

I scrolled down to find the response:

No.

Professor John Lane

That's it. No alternative routes or other related fields were suggested. I closed the browser. Students sat next to me, poking buttons on keyboards with their skinny fingers. I glanced at them on my way out; I'm sure one of them glanced at the email.

When I arrived home later that evening, I lay on my bed. I bent my head forward, and in between the rise and fall of my chest, I saw the chimney breast Blu-Tacked with A3 papers, scientific concepts scribbled on them. Diagrams. I let my head fall back on the pillow. The words of a conversation I had with my mother ten minutes ago pealed in the bedroom.

"You've lost a lot of weight. Me and your dad will not think less of you if you don't become a neurosurgeon. I won't let you kill yourself."

"None of you understand. I can't imagine myself doing something else. Being something else. I'm worth more than you know – I have to reach up for whatever I want to achieve."

I didn't look her way. The living room was a box, locked in tight around us. The walls seemed to draw us closer to the centre.

"You know, it's funny that you always say 'I don't want any of my sons to be like me and your dad who work shit jobs.' Now you're telling me to back off from my dream."

"If it means that you fall ill because of it, it's not something worth chasing. Think of something else to do. In this life God didn't allow it."

Her voice shook.

My dad's invariable response in multiple conversations was: "Drop this shit. Fuck it. What sort of sister-fucking life would you have lived if you did become a doctor? Long hours, no time to spend the money you earn. Listen, my friend's son did a course in optometry. He earns five hundred pounds a week, easy! Do that. Less stress, good money."

His small eyes widened behind his glasses, and his thick, bristly moustache and goatee curled and flexed every time he spoke. His meaty ball of a head blushed whenever the subject was brought up.

5:30am: I don't think about science anymore. I don't think about the brain. Dropping out of college and walking away from science, to pacing around with a tray under my arm, collecting letters, has kept me anaesthetised, though I sometimes feel the scars flaking.

"Come here, quickly."

I stride over to my line manager.

"Take these yorks out for me yeah?"

I follow a path to the loading bay with my now-gloved hands gripping the yellow bar of the york, minding people's feet, running parallel to other york-pushers. I look left and right. There are set-ups everywhere, semi circles of red-bagged yorks shrouding casuals. They hurl in parcels, dipping in and out of view as they bend down to grab handfuls from mini yorks. Mechanised doors to the loading area buzzes upwards and I enter a rush of cold air where hundreds of yorks are stood in zig-zags. I bend the label attached to the top of my york, have a look at where it needs to go. Bromsgrove. I push on and check the colour on the floor. I find Bromsgrove in the yellow section.

Once I've completed this errand, I am re-assigned to letter sorting again. Letters addressed to families and friends. Letters addressed to doctors at GP surgeries. I take my gloves off and grip a letter by the corners. I sense a pressure building at my eyes. I put my gloves back on. I throw the letter into a random pigeonhole. I don't care – I just want it out of my face.

5:45am: fifteen minutes 'til the end of my shift, and a short, stocky man (who doesn't wear a manager's hi-viz despite health and safety regulations) eyes us. I don't know his name; what I do know is that he spends the entire night shift walking, observing work speeds and ticking line managers off for reasons that are out of earshot. He puts his hands on his hips, confronting casuals with warnings.

He stops behind my line, claps his hands. "My two-year old son can sort quicker than you guys. I want to see those hands moving!"

His head bobs up and down as he walks in an affected gait, turning his head left and right at us.

I still ignore him, hands shaking, when he says to a fellow colleague: "You know what their problem is? They're not educated enough."

My feet are stuck to the ground. I can't get up and leave. I need the money.

My secondary school Maths teacher, Mr Hart, once explained to misbehaving students that, "You'll end up on the dole like those people who are happy to live their lives that way. Don't be them. Work for your success."

Class went on. Mr Hart started with easy Maths questions. I looked around. Students sat in silence. Those brave enough gave silly answers, and when asked to explain their methodology, backed down. I raised my hand. I answered. I was correct – and a few more times after that when no one else bothered.

I was writing an answer on the whiteboard when a student behind me shouted, "You think you're all clever don't you?"

"What's your problem?" I retorted.

"Don't get cheeky, I'll fuck you up."

After a friend backed me up, the idiot who spoke out went quiet, and I returned to my seat. I never locked eyes with him. I wasn't the type to get into punch-ups.

I remember leaning back in my chair and looking up at the ceiling, imagining that I could see the sky. I remember thinking that I was the best student amongst them, that I will never be them. I'll never claim JSA. I'll never work a shit job.

I'll transcend.

Jack Warren

Jack was raised in the West Country and was an award winning cocktail bartender prior to attending university. He lists Ted Hughes, R.S. Thomas and Gary Snyder as poetic influences.

Ad Infinitum

head down
to the church with broken windows.
Look amongst the graves and gravel
until you find it.

Carry it home at nightfall
Wrapped in burlap
hidden from rock-hail and rain
by your thick coat.

Burn firewood.
Feed it bread soaked in milk.
Bathe it's feet in lavender and warm water.
When it is strong enough to leave

pinch it's brittle ankles they will break
watch it crawl away
head down
to the church with broken windows.

Lack

No quarried rock cottage
with soot black hearth
nor woodland, nor fish, or axe.
There are no women with skinned knees
faces flushed from north sea wind.
No mongrels chew the bones of sheep
in the ice and clay.
A weavers hovel does not stake itself into the valley
and all along the line of Aspens, no single tree remains.

Hardwood

Years ago he planted feet.
The tread of steel-capped boot
in snow tight wood.
Grinning, muscle dense
he was fibrous structure
delighting in solemnity
with stomach clenched as if
awaiting some breath taking blow
and chest rising with the taciturn seasons.

He was killed not long after.
Cleaved in two and dragged
by rope to the city,
splintering in all directions
saw dust rising and flecking
the black hair of the commuters
who refused to look up as
his forearms scraped the concrete
pavement and he bellowed
through his gag.

He says now he suspects his life
will always be this furtive dash
from root to rock
and back again.
Cracking open beech seeds only
to discard their fruit.
Reading newspapers

longing for forest frost.
His mind is ablaze
but he says 'I am owed this'
and few can argue,
 he moves so fast.

Sheena Ramchurn

Sheena is currently in her second year of university, studying for an English and Creative writing degree with the intention of pursuing journalism in the future.

Forests in Winter

The lights are off in the women's dormitory but the spotlight outside is doing its nightly search around the camps. As the white beam circles around the guard tower, it breaches into the dorms and startles me awake. For a few seconds, I panic. Am I in trouble? No one hovers over me and the panic rescinds, replaced by a numbness that seeps into my bones. Shadowy bunks line the walls. Dust and skin flakes float up from the mattresses covering the bare floor. We sleep side by side like matchsticks. The elderly, pregnant or diseased sleep on bunks. The smell of shit, sweat, death and disease clings to the air and every night I fear the same. Whooping cough. TB. Whatever else festers in these beds and these women.

A few hours are left until morning so I try to ignore the recurring light and return to sleep. I press my arm hard into my eyes but it's useless. I'm too awake now. I'm uncomfortable, my joints ache, my stomach turns. It's bright and dark, and I'm sweating and shivering at the same time. Finally the spotlight switches off and I'm bathed in darkness again. There are a few groans of relief around the dorm. Half the women, like me, are awake. Sleep became a thing of the past the day we were dragged here. To me, that day seems like an invention of my mind. Did I really wear dresses? Apply lipstick? Go to school, dance, ride the bus? Or was that another girl? She seems like an old friend, someone I used to know. It's been so many years and I barely remember her face. The guilt in forgetting her is sometimes unbearable.

Someone coughs in the dorm which sets off a chain reaction and my ears fill with noise. Hacking coughs, groans. There is the soft sound of skin on skin as people turn against each other in their sleep. Bunks creak and a baby cries. The lady next to me begins weeping for her own baby back home, as she always does. As she rocks back and forth, she repeatedly bumps into me. I tune it out, tune it all out, and go back to the forest in my head.

I awake to darkness yet again come morning. Here, they wake us at 4am so we are ready to leave for work at 4.30. I have grown accustomed to this routine and wake up a minute before the alarm rings. Clockwork. I spend the minute running through my itinerary of the day. What do I have to do? I have to eat the bread I have stashed in my bra that I've been saving for six days. Any longer and the bread will be more blue than brown. I have to sort through my collection of papers and see if someone will patch the holes in my socks for a spare piece. I have to stay away from the guard with the blonde moustache and ginger eyebrows. He's a romantic. That's what we call them.

The tinny, shrill call of the alarm sends a shock through my veins. Just because I am used to the morning call, doesn't mean I'm not terrified of it. The numbness in me swells and hardens like concrete, blocking everything else out. It makes everything more tolerable.

A rattling sweeps through the dorm as the large door is pulled to the side, revealing the camp grounds. The first thing I see when I look out into the near darkness is the men. They have been released first today. A group of them sit near our building, waiting for us to come out, already leering. It's ok. Everybody leers here. The men, the guards, the women. It doesn't matter to me. Anyone can grope or touch me. They only feel the body, the concrete shell. What's inside is still mine.

Before leaving, I reach my fingers under the mattress and feel worn paper at my fingertips. They are letters from my lawyer, whom I haven't heard from in six years. I know in the back of my mind it's hopeless. My lawyer is probably dead. I keep them anyway.

As I shuffle out of the dorm with the rest of the female traffic, I pull out the bread from my bra and begin eating. In five minutes, I will make my way to the dining hall and convene with my work mates, those who work in the birthing units and make inmate cards for the newborns.

I pass a group of women nursing their babies together in the dark and a group of men licking rocks for sensory stimulation. It's a good idea but I could never bring myself to do it. A boy and girl reach their hands out to me, yearning for my piece of bread. I see my own siblings in their faces. Sliding past, I ignore them and sit alone near the fence.

This past month, there have been four births. All of them fathered by the guards. One guard took his baby home, the other left his outside to die of exposure, and the other two remain with their mothers to grow up alongside the rest of the unborn children.

As I nibble on my bread, I think of my brother and sister back home. The day my mother was arrested, we had all been separated. I am sure they are dead by now. If they are in camps like me, then I hope that they are.

An itch along my leg catches my attention and I look down to scratch it. Starting from my ankle and streaking up to my knee is a long, deep gash. The blood has long dried and now drifts from my skin as papery, red flakes when I scratch it. Some parts of the cut are scabbing, others are still open, exposing the pink-whiteness of my flesh. A certain inmate springs to mind, one who was chained to the wire fence and beaten by guards upon his arrival. The cuts across his body blackened and festered and he died on his third day. Some parts of my wound have blackened as well. It's beginning to seep out to the rest of the leg.

I look away, push down the bubble of panic, and stuff the rest of the bread into my face, savouring its salty taste and relishing the packed feeling in my mouth. After swallowing it down, I turn to stare at the grounds.

Beyond the labour camp, past the guard towers, the wire

fence and the electric fence, is a forest. It surrounds us. For the past six years, I have dreamed of walking through that forest in winter. To feel the cold snap of the air as it mumbles about the leafless, skeletal trees and wades softly between their ice cold barks. Blades of grass will stiffen and crunch underfoot as I walk about the soulless grounds.

Winds will whisper in my ear and an owl will shuffle in a tree branch, shaking powdery snow upon me. My breath will come out as curling vapour, my skin will turn ice cold and all that will remain of me is footprints embedded in the snow.

Malcolm Sanders

After a series of jobs in the UK and abroad Mal has settled into a cottage on the west coast of Ireland, next to the sea and eight miles from the nearest pub. He commutes to Birmingham, his home town, to attend the MA Writing and visit friends and family.

The Corridors

By the second winter there, he had grown several inches taller and was thin and pinched. His jacket now resembled a waistcoat. He would stuff the bits of lining that spilled out at the elbow back into the sleeves as best he could, which left his arms looking lumpy. The lining material was white and the jacket was black. Bits would hang out and the holes were spreading. It was all because he grew too fast. There was no point in having a coat if you grow too fast, he needed to wait for it to settle down. It was very cold that winter and even after running for most of the two miles every day he struggled to get warm and by the time he arrived he was even hungrier. The deputy sent for him again.

The corridor was designed around a quadrangle. It was difficult not to make too loud a noise unless you walked without putting your heels down. If you were in a hurry it was almost impossible, but hurrying was banned, like noise. If you were seen you would be stopped, which resulted in being in even more of a hurry. Being stopped may or may not be too bad but being late was always serious.

He heard the footsteps and knew they were being made by someone who wasn't afraid of making noise. The door he was aiming for was to his right and further along the corridor. It was tantalisingly close, but the corner from which the sound of footsteps was coming, was closer. He sped up with a sort of awkward trot for a couple of paces before the source of the footsteps appeared. As soon as the man's hand touched the polished brass knob the outcome was inevitable. He'd lost, the man stepped inside the room and slowly, deliberately and quietly closed the door behind him and waited for the click of the latch.

He had to open the door and enter immediately after, late by two steps. The man had taken a couple of paces and stopped. He leaned slightly forward, and slowly and deliberately, turned his upper body around to look at what had followed him into the room, and stare at it. With eyebrows raised and mouth open his upper body twisted as his right hand reached down and to his left. The jacket billowed like a cape as weight, momentum and timing combined to connect the back of this man's hand, with the face in front of him. It must have hurt his hand, the onlookers afterwards concluded, which would explain his subsequent mood.

As the hand caught the side of his face there was a squelch in his ear and a pain deep inside that made him vomit. There was nothing in his stomach to bring up.

"Get to assembly, all of you," the man said.

He didn't attend assembly, he never did. A door was opened and four of them walked in to the hall just for the notices. A religious thing, nothing to do with him and he never thought to question it. He was banned so that was the end of God in his life. It meant being paraded in front of a thousand others every morning in order to listen to the notices. He'd never been mentioned in them, it was mainly the first eleven. They were let in the side door by the monitor and were, whenever asked, grateful to participate in the liberal traditions of the school. It also meant that three times a week, instead of a scripture lesson, he could sit in the library undisturbed and read.

The coat was lying under a bench in the park. It was a spongy nylon thing and when he picked it up it felt heavy and it dripped water. There was nothing in the pockets. He held it at arm's length, wrung it out and took it to one of a line of derelict garages he'd discovered on his way home. The whole of the thin metal door to the garage was bent in a diagonal and it was easy to climb over and in. The interior was dark. He could make out a few empty paint tins, a pile of rags, beer cans and an old tyre.

The bits of old carpet on the floor were sodden and rotting with damp and diesel. By the time he had re arranged them it was too dark to see. He left the coat hanging from a door bracket and climbed out.

Two days later it was still there and still wet but already almost double its original size. He left it where it was, hoping that given a couple of more days it would stop smelling and dry out completely. There was one obvious problem with it and that was the colour. It was brown, but he was pleased nevertheless and vowed to keep his eyes open for a black one. The immediate problem was drying out the one he had in this weather, and getting rid of the smell. The next morning was as cold as he could remember. The frost on the pavements made running too hard so he walked as fast as he could in the hope of a few minutes at a hot radiator when he arrived. The first lesson was swimming. The baths were warm, and like several others with perforated eardrums, he was not expected to join in and it was not an ailment for which a note was required.

On the way home it started to snow and he saw a few inches of a wooden packing crate sticking out of a bin that was perfect for what he wanted. He enjoyed the snow, it was raw and unpredictable and wild. It reminded him of places on the tv. It changed his surroundings, the ground, the houses, everything. It made the lights coming from buildings look cosy in a way that never would happen ordinarily. It made the canal look cleaner and the bridges adventurous. He liked the snow especially when the wind caught it. He liked to look up and watch as it passed through the light of the streetlamps. It made his life different. It made him dream of afterwards and far away and secrets and going. Nobody took any notice as he pulled a newspaper from a bin and bits of a broken window frame from a skip.

In the garage he pulled a tyre from the back wall and dragged it to a dryer part of the floor, sat down on it and leaned against the wall. He pried the thin wood of the packing case apart along its grain into a dozen finger sized pieces. The snow outside dampened sound and made the little world he was beginning to create seem more his own and further away. He made a ball of paper and placed the slivers of wood on top in a pyramid. He had always made fire. He took one of the three matches he kept tucked down the ankle of his sock, and lit the paper. The small fire lasted, smoke free, about ten minutes. Enough time for him to feel the warmth and the jacket to start steaming. It felt cold and soggy quickly enough after the fire had died, but he was pleased.

He lived through the bells of the next day and was feeling almost excited as he slid over the broken garage door. The jacket was damp rather than wet and didn't smell as bad and he wanted to get the fire going to dry the thing out completely. He decided it was better to plan properly. He placed the remaining wood of the window frame at an angle to the wall and stamped on it until he had broken it down into usable lengths and made a neat stockpile of them in a dry corner. There was kindling left over which he put on the top of the wood pile but the newspaper was damp. He could find more on his way home tomorrow and he made a mental note to bring a few more matches before he had a quick look around the garage, turned the jacket inside out, put it back on the bracket and left.

Next morning he was earlier to the radiator in the cloakroom and even listened to the prayers and hymns though the door of the hall. When assembly had finished he was ready to open the door himself and was first in of the four of them for notices. The little parade at the side entrance of the hall was so much an accepted part of everyone's day that it went without comment, although there had recently been sniggers as his uniform got tighter. It crossed his mind what would happen if his name ever came up in notices and the whole of the room would have a reason to stare at him, but couldn't think of that ever happening.

"Sixteen an 'arf miss," after the French test.

"You may speak to your friends like that but you don't speak to me like that," she said

"Sixteen and a half miss."

The women tended not to hit out or pull hair but it was still a shame because he'd thought he'd done ok. At lunch time he went over to the wooden shelter in the park to look for fag ends. He was lucky and found two with a good bit left of them, lit up, looked out from the shelter and fantasised about finding someone's sandwiches. He had once or twice. A thin dusting of snow still covered the narrow paths of the park and everything looked new.

The garage was dark and he waited until he could make out the little woodpile and the jacket. He sat by the wall and took a small book from his pocket. The covers were gone and half the pages were missing. The writing was in two columns and the paper was very thin. He'd found it tucked behind a radiator in the cloakroom and had recognised immediately that those pages would be perfect to start his fire. He tore a few out, crumpled them loosely and arranged them in a little pile on the floor. The thinner sticks he rested on top of the paper and the larger pieces he kept to hand. He took out the matches from his sock, struck one on the floor and touched it to the paper. It caught immediately and he waited no more than a minute before placing a few of the larger sticks on top. He'd discovered that if he kept the wood going on to the flames slowly, one piece at a time, there was much less smoke. It was difficult to tell how wet the coat was because it felt so cold. When it started to steam he kept it moving in his hands over the heat. He was careful not to get it too near as the nylon would have melted and the spongy white stuffing spill out. There was enough fuel in his store to keep things going. He rocked forward, closer to the flames and smiled. It wasn't a good coat but he'd found it himself and brought it back to life and when he put it on, for the first time, it not only fitted, it was warm.

He kept it beside him in bed that night and put it on warm the next morning. The plan was to wear it so far and then stuff it into a plastic bag. Anyone seeing him carrying it, he thought, would assume it was his lunch or kit or something. He mustn't be seen in it, and a brown coat would stand out more and more against the black ones the closer he got.

It worked, the coat was warm and didn't smell. He sat in the shelter in the park and stuffed it in a plastic bag tying the handles together so that the colour of the contents could not be seen. In the cloakroom rows of coats were hanging on hooks like meat in an abattoir, below them were the benches. He stuffed his bag into one of the open wire cages underneath at the far end of the room.

Whenever he saw the deputy he always thought that the top half of his face starting at a horizontal line below his nose, looked as though it was about to sink into the bottom half. Normally that thought amused him. The deputy was sitting and his stare went from the coat to the boy. It looked filthy against the shine of the office floor.

"I'm a realist as well as a liberal. I know it's not murder, it's not stealing, but in a place like this it's about as fundamentally bad as you can get, do you know what fundamentally means? It's so deliberate, it must be, you in brown and everyone else in black, unless you are entirely stupid, or worse attempting to make us look stupid. Did you really think you wouldn't be seen? Do you really think I'm stupid? Do you think everyone else is stupid?"

There was a knock and the boy's eyes flicked to the door. That was enough for the deputy. He stood up took a step forward, grabbed a handful of hair and pulled the boy's head down to waist height. With his other hand he formed a fist. It was the backhand movement that caused his left cheek, just underneath the eye, to swell almost immediately. The deputy sat back down at his desk and wrote something. He was looking away from the boy as he spoke.

"Do you know why you are being punished?"

"I looked at the door, sir."

"No not that one, before that, in the first place. Stop being deliberately stupid."

"Wearing the wrong coat, sir."

"No. Principles and standards. If we don't stand for something, we fall over. Now do you understand?"

"Yes, sir."

"Get that signed by a parent, I want it back tomorrow, detention today. Get to assembly."

"Not allowed in assembly, sir."

"Oh yes of course. Well get someone to forgive you and make sure you're in for notices."

The deputy, kicked the brown coat into a corner, wrote 'please dispose' on a piece of paper which he placed on top of the little heap.

He put the detention slip in an inside pocket and felt the jacket's tightness across his shoulders. His face was ok after a while, except if he touched it. He was left alone and allowed his own world for the rest of the day. There was a kind of truce and he was even allowed to lean on the radiator in French.

Inside, the rooms had been cold all day, and he knew what to expect outside. It was almost dark. The pavements were slippery and he didn't feel like running anyway. He doubted even that would warm him up. He was tired and any semblance of wonder at the re painting of his world had left him. He tried to cram his fingers into his trouser pockets but only managed one hand at a time.

Inside the garage the darkness was complete and he was shaking. He felt for the paper and the remnants of the wood and they were where he had left them, he knew he had only one chance to get the fire started and it was crucial everything was ready before he lit one of his three matches. Inside it was drier of late and the fire warmed him quickly but he needed more fuel. There was enough of a glow to see into the pile of rubbish at the back wall and he found a few paint tins and a pile of rags that still smelt of oil. He thought the rags might burn and so stuffed them into a couple of the tins, thinking he might make a small version of the braziers that were to be seen outside the factories. He could find nothing to make holes in the tins so he put them down beside him, sat back on his tyre and leaned against the wall. Without fuel there was no alternative but to go home. He could find his way out in the dark so he sat leaning against the wall to watch the last of the glowing sticks pulse and writhe and, warm for the first time that day, he shut his eyes.

The rags had been very dry and although there would not have been any flame, the smoke they gave off was thick. Even so it was some time before anyone noticed and called the fire brigade. In assembly there was a speech outlining how we are each given opportunities and choices along the way and some of us make the right choices and some prefer not to and go their own way. He of course would have missed it anyway, as did the small group standing outside the door waiting to be let in for notices.

Sam Terne

Sam Terne is originally from London but now lives in Birmingham. She enjoys writing fiction, poetry and her satirical news blog: http://ternereport.blogspot.co.uk/. 'The Statue' is a modern retelling of a Welsh folk tale.

The Statue

Mike used to be nice to his wife Amy. He had married her in the 1990s, full of admiration and love. But now, he was tired of her. He found her conversation boring. Even the way she spoke had started to get on his nerves. He didn't talk to her about his annoyance, but he did start to be mean to her. Getting at her for not cutting the carrots in the right way. Dictating what they watched on television.

Amy tried her best to understand and forgive Mike's behaviour. Maybe he was depressed? Maybe he was finding work frustrating? She talked to her mother and her friends about it, who all reassured her that it was probably nothing to worry about and that it would probably blow over.

But it didn't.

He started saying little things to demean her. He started deliberately trying to embarrass her in front of their friends. And then he started to become spiteful. One day, he emptied the food waste recycling bin into one of her handbags because he said she shouldn't have put the banana from the fruit bowl into it.

"It was still ok to eat! I don't mind if they turn brown!"

Amy started to feel overwhelmed. They were a well off couple, her and Mike. Mike was an accountant, and Amy was a teacher. They had a nice house in Gypsy Hill, an area of South East London. Their house sat near the River Effra, which flows from near the Westow House pub, down the middle section of Jasper Road following the railway tunnel.

Amy had always loved where they lived, and she loved the river in particular. Sometimes she would go and walk along it to clear her thoughts. As Mike's behaviour towards her became more unkind, she made a habit of visiting the river every day. One day, on her way back from the river, she noticed a 'For Sale' placard up outside her house. She already knew what this meant, but instead of feeling angry, she just felt hopeless.

Inside, Mike was sitting at the kitchen table. He was drinking a glass of beer and smoking.

"You know I don't like you smoking in the house."

"It's not your house anymore. I'm getting rid of it. I've got my eye on a smaller flat, in town. I've already done two viewings and made an offer. We'll probably move there."

Amy sat down opposite him at the table. She wanted to speak, but didn't have the words.

Later that night, she got up from their shared bed as he was sleeping. She walked downstairs, put her trainers on, and went outside, shutting the door behind her. She walked down to the river, which was flowing calmly in the moonlight. Walking down the river path, she collected as many stones as she could, putting them into the pockets of her nightdress as she went. When she felt she had enough, she slowly walked into the river, deeper and deeper.

The accountant woke the next morning to find his wife gone. He looked for her in the house and in the garden, but couldn't find her. Worrying that he would be late for work, he left, thinking that she had maybe gone to her mother's last night. *Maybe she's angry about me putting the house up for sale*, he thought.

When he got home from work, he continued looking for her, but couldn't find her. Eventually, he went down to the river to see if she was there. He followed it down, past the Westow House, past the Paxton pub, along the back garden line of Croxted Road, until the point where the river joins its other branch at the South Circular. There, it forms the sewers of Croxted Road, Dulwich Road, Dalberg Road, Effra Road, Electric Lane, Brixton

Road and Harleyford Road, separated by the Kennington Oval. And that's where he found Amy, in her nightdress and trainers.

He looked at her face and ran away, back along the garden line, until he reached the house. The guilt he felt caused him to rip the 'For Sale' placard up out of the ground in front of the house, but as he did so, he turned to stone.

Months passed and the stone statue remained stationary, but at midnight on the 20th June, it woke up. With heavy steps, it walked along the river, all the way to sewer, calling Amy's name as it went, trying to persuade her to come back. By dawn, the statue was back, in front of the house in Gypsy Hill. The statue did this year after year, always at the same time of midnight on the 20th June. No one noticed, until one June, four years after Amy's suicide, a passerby on his way home from the pub noticed the statue moving. At first the onlooker thought he was having a drunken hallucination, so he called his friend. The two friends followed the statue along the river, not being able to believe what they were seeing.

Since then, the people of Gypsy Hill whitewash the statue once a year so they can see him coming when he follows the river along the back garden line of Croxted Road. The house has never been sold.

Siren Knight

Siren Knight is a writer from Birmingham, currently undertaking a Masters in Writing. She describes herself as terminally nocturnal and a shameless over-writer. Siren confesses that she enjoys deliberately leaving a piece of hidden eggshell in her breakfast omelette and playing Russian roulette with herself first thing each morning.

Dark Fire

Have you been crying down my window pane again?
They've read all my words so they all know your name
You keep bleeding on these pages
Your darkness is contagious
I was always pathetic for the things I can't tame

Every morning you wake up with claw marks on your skin
But you never know if something is trying to escape or
    get back in
How tortured are your dreams?
Darling, how deep?
And who is it that gets to watch you scream in your sleep?

I have a habit of writing things on dark walls
Would you stay if I admit that that last line was yours?
No, I can't help but be attracted to
Those things inside of you
That howl when darkness falls

Every morning you wake up with claw marks on your skin
But you never know if something is trying to escape or
    get back in
How tortured are your dreams?
Darling, how deep?
Maybe I could be the reason you smile in your sleep?

How much of my despair do you actually require?
There is blood in the breeze which I think you inspired

Did you hear that I traded my blood in for ink?
Darling it's not what you think
I was always paper and you are still fire

You are a dark fire burning inside of me
Don't blow on my embers put me out my misery
You are a dark fire burning inside of me
Blow on my embers put me out my misery

No Ball Games Allowed

I watch you watch me as I ingress
Though you feign that you do not
Betraying eyes linger on my dress
Trembling fingers down a shot
An array of introductions
And I laugh louder than all
Those aqua eyes burn with seduction
Yet you're cemented to the wall
Later on a shocked expression
A faltered 'I didn't know you were here'
I smirk in my discretion
And let you lie right in my ear
   So I guess it's games we're playing, don't be the first to fall
   I down another Sambuca and wait for you to pass the ball

Letter to His Mistress

Dear _____,

I stare as you uncoil out in front of him, lurching so far forwards that you almost lap against his feet.

You linger for a moment in his eye line, a wild creature deciding on the fate of a new prey. I see his eyes flash in amusement, in the way of someone who has stumbled upon a worthy adversary. A way that he has not looked at me before, and I am astute enough to muster up a terror for that look and let it embed itself as an anchor into the lining of my stomach.

Somewhere, someone grasps the elbow of their lover and draws him backwards.

Weeks pass and the look does not leave him. I promised him that once we got here I would quit the 'cancer sticks' but I have doubled up to almost twenty a day...we have already settled the payment on the new house.

And you, you are already the other woman aren't you...or worse, am I?

This was supposed to be our refuge, mine and his, our slice of heaven, our 'up yours' to the society that would have us believe we must work our days away in cubicles. I was going to write and he was going to find his passion. Is the joke on me? Are you it?

We are here again, standing here again and you are here again. He says not to worry, don't be silly. He has known you since he was a little boy. That you had always played together in his childhood, yet his eyes glaze over as he says that it takes the travelled mind of an adult to appreciate what you really are, to ingest your beauty, to osmose your power, and I close my eyes and pretend that it is me he is talking about. Childishly, I draw nearer to him, he holds me against him and I allege to myself to have no knowledge of you watching him, watching you, over my head.

Weeks become months and I am a passenger in my own life story. A disposable, optional character. I do not know where I have gone.

At night I lie awake in our little house and we can both hear your whispers. Your siren song calls out to him and I lay in a tentative state, dread snaking through my stomach. Some nights he shuts his ears to you and spoons against me, closing you out, and I cling to those moments; a limpet to a crag.

But others you are insatiable and he is so restless, so easily swayed and I am left ridiculous.

He goes out to you, his fingers fretting for the feel of his board beneath them, and I am never permitted to accompany him. So I sit and imagine how he watches you before plunging into you, watching your curves as you dance back and forth for him in the moonlight. How beautiful you must look, rising up and down, back and forth, how breathless he must be. How awed he is by your savageness, how he is almost scared of your venomous moods. And how in other moments you are so soft that you slip through his fingers and trickle down his spine, so delicate and feminine that it is almost like you are not even there. A dream that he cannot quite believe he has been permitted to be a part of.

And I imagine how he climbs into you, feels the pull of you beneath him as you become one, moving in and out as one creature. Is it merely routine for you? Are you even aware he is there? Or do you enjoy it as much as he does?

When he returns back to my bed he is wet with your scent and his spirit is calm. You have satisfied his desire and I am hopeless in your talons.

I spend my days searching for properties inland, hopeless searches for houses in cement forests, brick views and grey airs. He laughs at my findings and puzzles over my sudden change in direction. Didn't you want this? He says. Is this not why we are here? And how can I say yes, but not like this. How can I say that I hoped I was enough. That I was his passion?

Months taunt at a full year and your affair has become a nightly occurrence. I can no longer hold him in my bed, always he must flee to you. Always you are waiting, beckoning him with your salacious whispers of mystery; freedom. All the virtues that I used to possess, that I have traded in for jealousy; bitterness.

It seems I have become the mistress in the relationship of an immortal, and I am awful and pathetic and every evening I sleep alone.

On the night that it happens. I beg him to stay.

You are so desperate this night, so terrible and venomous. I can hear you crashing yourself against the eaves of the house, demanding his presence, demanding his attention. *She will kill you*, I shriek. An empty vase shatters in my state, stagnant water screams across the floor. *She will be the death of you.* My hands are shaking. I've left my cigarettes in the car. *A storm is coming, you cannot go to her! You will be caught in it.* But my pleas are wasted on his stubborn ears and I am so sad, so sad that there is nothing in my mere mortal body that will make him stay.

I lie on my back and I watch the ceiling. The ceiling I have come to know so well, and I hear the way the storm breaks itself against the window just like I knew it would. Just like I warned him. But he is always so stubborn, he is experienced now he says, almost pro. And you, you are so undeniable.

The rain snarls and scratches outside,hurling itself against the windows. Thunder shouts through every crack in the wooden slats of the house, roaring through every hole. Lightning scurries between the black clouds, cracking its tail against them and lending it's blinding light for mere seconds at a time. I torture myself at the open door but it is so pitch black and devoid of mortals out there that I am confined to the restriction of the wooden door frame and I cling to it, pathetic, desperate. My own common sense holds me prisoner, and forces me to cower, inside the body, inside my house.

When the storm reaches the ocean and I see lightning dip her tail into the black waves I retreat back into the house. I cannot stand to watch the scene of a massacre. Thunder reaches down and rattles the roof. I cower, I cower. I count the hours in the way I watch the night use the window as its medium and flaunts its travels across that ceiling. I watch as it moves across the sky in an exhausted half slumber and gives way to the unyielding power of the sun rise. It has been so long, too much time has passed. He has not returned. The phone hangs on its noose, suspended in mid air. My guilty hands shake with apologies, my cigarettes are in the car.

Long before the formal knock on the front door at midday, I know he is gone and that you have taken him, just as I knew from the beginning that you would.

They serve me a death sentence with their apologies, with their 'nothing they could do's'.

My body falls from around me to the floor like an unzipped dress.

I am a ghost.

I am vomit.

Time has no use here, I have long forgotten its rules.

There is a dripping on my face, someone's left the tap on.

A brash laugh out loud, a cackle, because even they, even they belong to you don't they? Even the saltwater of my own body will find its way back to you and I am defeated and resigned to let them trickle down my cheeks and present themselves as sacrificial gifts to you.

You lover, you temptress, you murderer.

Years slip into a decade and still I linger here. I have tried so many times to leave but your whispers caught in shells and crevices always seem to promise of his return. I can't bare to be away from you.

Every night I am drawn to the same place, where he used to watch you and prep his board. Now I come to watch you as you tolerate the moon pulling you back and forth. Some nights you are so angry there is no calming you. Your rage is so powerful and you spit out at me, taunting me and I scream back at you and you never ever care.

Will you ever show me? Show me the way you swept him further and further away from me that night?

Did he ever look back? Was he scared? Did he think of me? Or were you such a distraction that he went willingly along your curves? Did you pin him down to your bed? And move against him in a way that I could never quite manage? You did, didn't you. You adulterer, you murderer!

And I beg you, I beg you to take me as well, to lay me in your bed. But I am already so broken that you have no use for me. So I beseech you to crack open my ribs and drain me, purge me, of every feeling, every memory I have. For I am so haunted, so exhausted.

Yet you do nothing, except continue to stomach my awful presence. Continue to rock slowly, in and out, with a calming manipulative serenity that I begrudgingly admire. And I look out into you, your endless liquid ink. Look at the way I have splashed the ink across my pages and laugh at my own handiwork.

I am writing to you. To you.
You distraction.
You darkness.
You nightmare.
You beautiful, beautiful thing.

I am writing you a letter. A letter to his mistress, a letter to his murderer...a letter to the sea.

Ian Marchant

Ian Marchant is a writer, performer, singer, broadcaster, and creative writing tutor at Birmingham City University. Originally from Newhaven in Sussex, he now lives in the non-existent Welsh county of Radnorshire. He is working on a history of the British counter-culture entitled 'A Hero For High Times', due for publication by Cape in 2016.

X meets Y. They fall in love. Due to circumstances beyond their control, they part.

Here's an old story. Set, in this particular translation, in St. Petersburg. In the 1880's, shall we say?

X is married, happily up to a point, with two daughters he adores. He is comfortably situated, a writer with a tenured post at the University, and a dutiful and loving wife who keeps a warm and welcoming home. His novels are translated into French, German and English; and he is well known, widely respected and sought after in company. Y is in a similar social position, with a hard-working husband (a high ranking railway official of some kind) who worships her, a son she loves and for whom she harbours ambition. She is quiet, Finnish, quick to smile. X is older than Y, by almost 20 years.

X and Y have met a few times at the theatre in the company of mutual acquaintances, and have nodded at one another, and exchanged a few words. Y has an identical twin sister, called Z, who is also a theatre-goer, and who also moves within the outer reaches of X's circle of friends.

At the moment of the beginning of this telling of the story, X did not know the names of either Y or Z. He thought of them as the Finnish sisters, if he thought of them at all. If he had been asked, he could not have told Y and Z apart.

Early one morning, whilst walking in the Summer Garden, X saw a woman at some distance, coming towards him, the low sun from behind lighting her white hair like a halo. He could imagine her shape against her clothes.

He thought, 'That is a beautiful woman. Although she is too far away for me to see in detail - whether she is young or old, I cannot tell, (though the colour of her hair leads me to suspect that she is perhaps in her early sixties) – I can see that this woman is a great beauty.'

As she came closer, X saw that the woman was not in her sixties, but rather in her mid-thirties.

Closer still, X realised that the woman was, in fact, Y – Y and not Z. And X further realised, therefore, that Y was very beautiful.

He raised his hat. She smiled, and stopped, and spoke as if they were old friends.

"Oh, X," she said. "I am glad to have met you, you of all people. I have been so worried about my son. He is doing badly at school, but I am sure that's because it is the wrong school for him. I'm wondering if I might find him a place at the Classical Gymnasium... I'm sure you are the man to tell me." He noticed that, despite her accent, she spoke beautiful Russian.

"Of course. It will be a pleasure to tell you what I can."

Y talked of her son's troubles at school, while X listened. From time to time, she would look up at him from under her fringe, and smile. X smiled back, and told her what he knew of the Classical Gymnasium, and how she might find her son a place there.

Then Y said, "My husband is not interested. He does not love our son. He said to me last night that he wishes our son was grown-up, and moved away." She looked up at X, and pushed her hair back from her face.

"I'm sure..." said X, thinking to find some conciliatory words. But he could not find them. He did not understand how a father could not love his child. Her beauty had come as a surprise, and it unsettled him.

"It has been a pleasure to talk... but I must get to my office."

"I have kept you," she said.

"Not at all. Not at all… but…"

"I understand."

"Perhaps we'll meet again. Let me know if I can help with your son."

Again, he raised his hat, and they parted.

For the next few days, X thought of Y, thought of her openness and trust, and her smile, and he found himself smiling in turn.

Ten days or so later, X was making his way home after dining with friends. It was an evening such as can only be experienced in Petersburg, a June evening, still with some light of the sun in the western sky, but also with a full moon overhead, and a few stars visible in the east. He stopped - to tie his bootlace, or to fumble in his pockets for matches - when Y came round the corner. They almost collided.

X said, "I'm sorry, it is so rude of me, but I don't know your name."

Again, that smile.

"Y," she said.

"I'm X"

"I know. Which way are you going? May I walk with you?"

"It would be a huge pleasure. How is your son getting on?"

They walked for an hour, turning this way and that, rather than take the streets which might cause them to part. Y spoke of her childhood; summers by the side of a Finnish lake, clearing snow from the street outside her Grandfather's house.

"I have never been to Finland. I am told it is very beautiful. I would love to go."

"Go in summer. To the Lakes. It is very beautiful."

"You could come and be my translator."

Y laughed.

"I would be little use; I am from Åland; my first language is Swedish. Besides, everyone speaks Russian! You'd be fine. I have a book at home about Finland, in Russian. With illustrations. Would you like to see it?"

"Very much."

They stopped at a turning where it was clear they could no longer postpone going in opposite directions.

"Is your home far from here?" asked X.

"Not far, X. We are almost neighbours. Do not worry about me; I'm sure I won't be attacked."

"Goodnight Y', said X, using her name for the first time.

'What a charming mistress she would make', thought X as he came up to his front door. 'It is some years since I've taken a mistress, but I feel ready again. I have the discretion necessary to keep a mistress, though a married mistress with a son will pose new challenges. But, no, it will be worth it. I shall show her great respect.' A few days later, however, it became clear to X that his wish to make Y his mistress was not going to be possible, for the following complicating reason; he had fallen in love with her.

He had been riding in a carriage on Nevsky Prospekt when he saw Y come out from Gostiny Dvor with a large bunch of sweet peas (presumably just bought from a florist inside the arcade). She buried her face in the flowers, her white hair framing the blooms. Witnessing this sensual act, X felt himself lift from his seat. As the carriage hurried past, he turned, and waved, almost toppling over; and she smiled and raised her flowers in greeting. He craned his neck to see her, and watched her disappear into a dot.

X felt as though he had swallowed a melon, whole, which now sat in his stomach. X dropped back into his seat.

The carriage driver called, "Is everything alright, Sir?"

"Yes, thank you," said X, but he knew it wasn't true. Everything was not alright. He had read his Stendhal, and he knew what had happened. At first, he was indifferent to the charms of Y, had not noticed them at all. Then, after he noticed them for the first time in the park, and most especially after the evening walk, he felt hope that he might be able to enjoy those charms in a civilised manner. But in that momentary glimpse of Y with her face in flowers, all her imperfections had become charms, and all her charms turned to shimmering crystal.

X was angry with himself. 'It is true' he thought, 'there is no fool like an old fool. Y would make such a fine mistress; but I have fallen in love with her, and this cannot be. I cannot betray my wife like that. I am a man of honour. It is unfortunate (and painful) but it cannot be helped. I am not ready for a mistress, after all.'

But now, his every waking thought was of Y, and when he could see her again. He had no way of contacting her; and knew that this was good. 'This will pass,' he thought, 'as it passed when I was a callow youth, first come up to Petersburg, and fallen in love with my tutor's daughter.'

Ah, but he longed to see Y!

When next he saw her, a few days later, it was once again in the park, though this time she was walking with her son. She laughed, and pulled her hair away from her face. Her son fidgeted while X and Y talked.

"I have not forgotten that I promised to lend you that book," she said.

As they talked, and greatly to his surprise, X found that he had, quite unintentionally, dropped all his guards. When last he had found himself in this state, thirty and more years ago, he had been unable to say so much as good-day to his tutor's daughter; but now he talked to Y as though she was the only person in the whole of Russia who could possibly understand him. He talked as he had not talked for years. And she listened to him. To flirt with this woman was one thing, a game which might once have been amusing, but to talk to her like this; from his heart – this was not a game; it was ruination. He knew that to talk this way was to threaten all that he held close; and must lead to the loss of his daughters, and therefore his life. And with her standing before him, when X heard her voice, her laugh, he could feel the abyss opening beneath his feet. Yet he could not stop himself.

For twenty minutes or more they stood talking.

Y's son continued to fidget.

"You have been very patient, young man. I hear you're trying to get into the Classical Gymnasium. If you are as patient with your books, I'm sure you'll pass the entrance exam."

"What do you say?" said Y.

"Thank you, Sir."

"We shall be friends, I'm certain."

Y looked up at X, and touched his arm.

"Thank you X," she said.

He made his way home in rage and joy. Rage at himself, (he could hardly bear to admit it to himself, but it had to be faced) for falling in love. Joy, because she had touched him. Rage, because he could not be friends with Y, or take her as his mistress, as he had hoped. Joy, joy, because he loved her.

Finding his wife and daughters not at home, X sat in his study, and tried to concentrate on a recent issue of a philological journal. He heard a carriage in the street, and the doorbell ring; and moments later he stood up, dropping the journal to the floor, as the servant announced Y.

"I hope you don't mind... but I've brought you that book about Finland."

"Mind? No, of course not... please, will you have some tea? Marta... tea for two."

"No, I don't want to intrude."

"Of course, you must. I insist. Marta, the tea."

And so Y sat in X's study for an hour. He sat with his hand on his chin while she talked of her sister Z, of her parents, of her coming to Petersburg. And when the clock chimed four, and she rose to leave, Y said,

"Thank you for letting me waste your time."

"My dear Y, talking to you is the best possible use I could make of my time, I assure you."

He showed her to the door himself, and the smile that she gave as she turned and walked down the steps to the street would stay in his memory always, to burn and to console.

Yet how could she behave like that? How could she dare to come here? What if his wife had been at home, or his daughters? And what was he thinking, inviting her for tea? Old Marta might gossip to the other servants, and then his wife would surely come to hear of the visit. And what then? What would he say to his wife if she asked him who his caller had been? It was clear what course he must take. He must tell his wife that Y had called, and then he must see Y no more. But, the sound of her voice. The trust she showed him in her talk, and the ease with which he could talk to her. That smile as she turned to leave. The melon he had been holding in his stomach for weeks turned over.

And X did not tell his wife when she returned.

He did not see Y again for almost a fortnight; a fortnight in which he thought of her through all his days. But once in that time he saw Z, at the theatre; and he knew it was Z. It was extraordinary to him that it should be so clear which sister he loved, when they appeared identical at first glance. But as X looked he saw that Z's face was harder than Y's, and less quick to smile - and the closer he looked, the more the resemblance slipped away.

One afternoon, he was walking through Gostiny Dvor looking for a present for one of his daughters and he thought, 'Here I am, and I don't know when I'll ever see her again. It might be never; Petersburg is big, our paths might simply not cross - or she might move away, and I might never see her again, never know where she had gone. Or, I might turn the next corner and...'

And she was there. She was there. Round the next corner.

And they were next to the door of a tea house.

And he invited her to join him, and she agreed;

"Though I'm not really dressed..." and, again, they talked, and again, the clock chimed, four, five, six, this time unnoticed.

But now it chimes seven.

She stands up, with her hand over her mouth.

"Oh! My son! I promised I would kiss him goodnight."

"Then, you must go, dear Y."

He walks her to the door of the tea house. They stand on the pavement, looking at one another, not speaking. And then she takes a step closer to him, and turns her face to him, and blushes, and says,

"I hope we meet again soon."

And he takes her face in his hands, and he kisses her.

Here is a turning point in the story. They have become lovers. How is their affair to be conducted? Do they sit together in the park, or in cafes holding hands under the table? Do they write letters? How often do they meet, and what is said between them? Do they arrange it so that they can make love? If so, how is it arranged? It hardly matters. Happiness, for both of them, whatever form it takes, can now only be found in one another's company. When they are apart, it is torture. When they are with their families, it is a living horror. Y cannot allow her husband to touch her, which breaks his heart. X feels a deep compassion for his loving wife, and holds her close to him, trying to give her comfort and strength. His wife sees that X is unhappy, and insists that they visit Koktebel on the Black Sea coast for a month. But X's unhappiness deepens whilst they are away. During his absence, Y is frantic. She does not eat during the month, and on his return, when X and Y meet at last, she is weightless in his arms.

And so it carries on; for a season? A year? Several years? But it cannot last. A final crisis is reached. Are they perhaps discovered, unmasked, threatened with exposure? I do not think so, because they are not ashamed. In one of Chekhov's versions of this story, perhaps one of his best known, X and Y realise that, despite everything, despite all the pain it will cause to their families, they have to be together. I do not think our X and Y have that choice, because they both feel that they cannot find a lasting happiness in the shadow of the misery of others. In the great telling of this story by the English writer Evelyn Waugh, Y tells X that she must leave him, because to be together is a sin in the eyes of God. That doesn't seem quite right in this case, though I suspect our lovers faced a moral crisis – Y's husband being taken ill, or X's wife being discovered by her husband crying in loneliness and desperation, knowing that she is betrayed, but not how.

Or it could be that they realised at the same moment that the time for their parting had come; yes, that seems right. They part, after a last desperate meeting, by mutual agreement; and it cannot be borne.

It cannot be borne. X keeps a pearl handled pistol in the secret drawer of his bureau. He takes it out, loads a bullet, and holds it in his lap. Y stares into the black waters of the Neva, and thinks she might find peace there. She takes a step.

But then something happens.

Perhaps X has forgotten to lock his study door; a child runs in laughing, and asks for help with her French grammar. Perhaps Y sees moonlight on the water, or hears music from a high window. She steps back. Something has changed. Y cries; X hugs his daughter to him, and whispers I love you into her hair.

And so life, diminished, continues. Over time, grief turns from a wound to a bruise. Bruises must be shielded, or they can still cause pain. X avoids the Summer Garden in particular. In spring, there is an unusual cherry tree with white blossom, the white of her hair, which he cannot bear to see. He also avoids the theatre so far as possible, but professional obligation means that X must from time to time attend performances, though he excuses himself when he can, because it was at the theatre that he first saw Y. It is now never more than twice a year that he goes.

Once, perhaps nine or ten years since the parting with Y, X saw Z in an intermission for the first time in a long time, and pushed his way through the crowd towards her. They talked of the play. After a time, X said,

"How is Y? Please tell me something of your sister."

"Haven't you heard? Her husband died, and she has moved back to Mariehamn. Several years ago."

X felt his head spin, and was sure that he must faint.

"I did not know."

"Her son is an officer in the Army'"

"She... she has not remarried?"

"No."

"No. I should not have..."

"And you, X? You are well? Your wife is well? Your daughters?"

"They are well. My daughters are married. I am a grandfather."

"You are lucky."

"Do you write to your sister?"

"Of course. Once a month."

"Perhaps.... in your next letter.... you could tell her that we met. And that I am well, and a grandfather."

"I will. I know that you were friends. She spoke of you often. She will be glad to hear of it."

The bell rang for the second half of the performance. X took Z's hand, and pressed it to his lips.

Now, sometimes on summer evenings, X sits drinking tea in a café opposite the Finland station, watching for one among the newly arrived passengers emerging from the platforms in gouts of steam, watching for one who never comes.

Acknowledgments

Thank you to everyone who has participated in this project, without which, the book would have been impossible.

With special recognition to Rhoda Greaves, Greg Leadbetter, Sam Malkin, Sarah Wood, Patrick McGuinness, Mark Bracey, Rochelle McKiernan, to all those who have submitted to the Anthology, friends, family, and early morning coffee.

And to you, dear reader.
  Enjoy.